T

IN

CHALK

THROUGH PARTS OF

SOUTH WILTSHIRE

IN

1807

WRITTEN IN

𝕬 𝖘𝖊𝖗𝖎𝖊𝖘 𝖔𝖋 𝕷𝖊𝖙𝖙𝖊𝖗𝖘

ENCOUNTERING ON THE WAY; A CHARCOAL BURNER,

TOGETHER WITH A VISIT TO

STONEHENGE, FONTHILL ABBEY
AND STOURHEAD,

INTERSPERSED WITH VARIOUS ANECDOTES,
ANTIQUARIAN OBSERVATIONS AND BOLD VIEWS ON THE
PREHISTORY OF THIS LAND.

BY

A PEDESTRIAN.

EAST KNOYLE :

PUBLISHED BY THE HOBNOB PRESS

2005.

GW00383892

ADVERTISEMENT.

☞ *First published in 2005 by The Hobnob Press, PO Box 1838, East Knoyle, Salisbury SP3 6FA.*

© *'A Pedestrian' 2005.*

☞ *All illustrations are by the author.*

☞ *All rights reserved. No part of this publication may be reproduced, stored in a retrieval system, or transmitted, in any form or by any means, electronic, mechanical, photocopying, recording or otherwise, without the prior permission of the publisher and copyright holder.*

☞ *British Library Cataloguing in Publication Data: A catalogue record for this book is available from the British Library.*

ISBN 0-946418-42-X.

☞ *Typeset in Bodoni and designed by John Chandler.*

Printed in Great Britain by Salisbury Printing Company Ltd, Salisbury.

LETTER TO THE EDITOR

As the recipient of the following letters I hold myself entirely responsible for encouraging my young nephew to venture forth on such an undertaking when so inexperienced in life into such uncertainty and danger.

Had I realised that my own recent work; "A Pedestrian Tour of North Wales, 1805" would have inspired my Dearest Nephew so I would most definitely have resisted the small vanity that its publication provided. It was with increasing horror that I received and read the steady succession of correspondence knowing the extent of the sham on which his livelihood depended. The knowledgeable reading public will no doubt be aware of the plethora of published journals that proclaim adventures to all parts of our British Isles when in reality their authors set foot no further than visiting the tired accounts of others and in the event of any shortfall let their own limited imaginations complete the task. Let it be known that I am guilty of just such a crime for crime it will be if my own Nephew suffers harm on his own naïve quest.

It is with some desperate hope that this publication, in the form of my Nephew's letters to myself, will somehow fall into the hands of its young author and remind him of the trust he once placed in me and that in response he might again take up his pen to give even the smallest indication of his well being.

Yours faithfully

J. CHALK

November 1807

DEDICATION.

Everyone who has generously offered their wisdom and encouragement and to 𝕃, my nearest and dearest, for whom anonymity is simply unheard of.

Thursday 8th October 1807

MY DEAR UNCLE,

Your surprise in receiving this correspondence can
only be matched by my own in the writing of it. I find
myself engaged on a pedestrian tour in South
Wiltshire and when time permits I will divulge the
circumstances which lead to this undertaking but
suffice to say it did not suffer long in the formation of
a plan. Your own published account of a Tour of North
Wales has these past two years been an inspiration for
me to leave London and see with my own eyes the
world outside that overcrowded and stinking
metropolis. I hope one day to follow your own path
and visit Lake Bala and Beaumaris and also to ascend
Cadir Idris to contemplate the importance of the
human race from that great elevation. Now I have
before me John Cary's map of Wiltshire that I
obtained from a bookseller in Salisbury and across
this sheet my own adventures lay in store.

I reason that you will not be offended if I were to record my present activities, whatever they may be, in a series of letters to you my Dear Uncle and you can do with them what you will. However I flatter myself indeed that I can compete with you with either the pen or the pencil.

Travelling on the outside of the London to Exeter coach I have suffered the most severest shaking of my life. The inside of the coach being full I shared the roof with a cheerful Irishman and a not so jolly officer who is to sail from Falmouth when conditions permit. From amongst the jostling luggage I had watched Salisbury Cathedral spire grow slowly from the gentle folds in the landscape and with every revolution of the wheels I was willing it to rise up and tower above me knowing that only then by finding myself in its shadow would there be an end to the torture.

Finally we halted in the centre of Salisbury and after sliding down from my perch I found that I could not put one foot in front of the other and my left leg may as well have been constructed of wood such was the use of it which is not a desirable way to begin life as a pedestrian tourist. The only remedy for this

condition is to walk and so I hope Sir, you will forgive
me when I tell you that having longed to reach the
base of this great gothic spike, I then turned my back
on it and purchasing from a bookseller my new map I
then stumbled my way out of the city. Surely Mr
Camden and lately Mr Britton can furnish you with all
the pertinent details regarding Salisbury Cathedral:
the height, the width, the length, how many windows
and when the spire last caught ablaze etc..etc..etc..
Indeed I would be more pleased to encounter the
quarries themselves from which this rare stone had
been won in a county so renowned for its chalk rather
than be conducted on a weary tour of the building
itself. Please forgive my impertinence for I do not
really mean so. I promise to return to Salisbury but I
feel as a narrator my spirit should be free to explore
the unexplored, to see with new eyes and to record
exactly all that I witness. You will know well enough,
my Dear Uncle, that to follow the trail of another over
old ground is not the way of the adventurous
pedestrian tourist. I may as well sit in the comfort of an
old worn armchair and blow the dust from the yellowing
pages of the accounts of others before reaching for my

pen to concoct my own. That was not your way, nor shall it be mine.

At the miserable landmark that is Fisherton Gaol my thoughts and direction were distracted by the sight of the gibbet, occupied by some poor wretch who by the attentions of various carrion was made to swing and turn gently in the windless evening. Having missed the handpost I found myself on the road to Wilton rather than my intended destination toward the Avon Valley and Amesbury. At Wilton lies another target for the persevering tourist, Wilton House. Sir, I refer you in advance to Malpooles' New and Complete British Traveller to acquaint yourself with the complete list of paintings contained within and also to determine exactly which tree Sir Philip Sidney reclined against whilst dreaming of Arcadia. But what kind of account is this that skirts around the obvious and dwells even less on describing the incidental?

I had barely left the City boundaries when I took a fall. I had halted at the entrance to a brickworks to observe a cart load of fresh bricks leaving the yard for the city. Here was the source of the material for those fine new red brick buildings I had just observed in

Salisbury. The ruts in the road outside the entrance to this industry had been loosely filled with some large and incommodious nodules of stone and it was amongst these that I first stumbled and then fell, twisting my ankle and grazing the palms of my hands, with the pack on my back adding to the weight of the fall. As I lay there at the side of the road facing downwards, at first not a soul came to my assistance. A dog showed some interest in my pack, sniffing at the cheese and ham and another cart pulled around me. I hauled myself up into a sitting position and inspected my ankle, moving it slowly to and fro and I brushed off the loose grit from my grazed palms. You may wonder, Dear Uncle, why I am giving you an account of my fall and its aftermath when surely a fall is a fall is a fall and is to be expected by the pedestrian tourist. It was not the fall that interested me but what made the fall, the large ochreous nodules were, I believe, flint and were in the main rounded and natural looking yet one caught my eye as it was almost porcellaneous in appearance, flattish and very regular in shape like a large flat bottomed leaf. I picked it up and immediately felt the keenness of its edge which extended around all sides, yet the base of the piece was broad and blunt. You will know my amateurish peculiarities when confronted with interesting geological examples and here I sat in the road turning this stone around in my grazed hands noting how it fitted well into the palm as if it had been made so. The next cart out of the pit stopped before me, the heavy horses were blinkered but able to look down on this miserable wretch in the road, obviously wounded in his understanding of the world. The driver held his team back as two passers-by, a man and a boy, cheerfully assisted me to my feet and dusted me off but hastily departed before I could offer them something for their trouble.

Walking was now difficult, but curiosity regarding the provenance of this unusual stone led me to inspect the excavations within the brickworks. The working day was now drawing to a close and a huddle of pan-faced smokers in the yard observed me as I hobbled about the place. I found a pile of flint nodules of the same type that caused my fall and beyond these the pit itself, cut in ledges at different stages of excavation. I could determine the top soil and beneath that perhaps ten feet of earth suitable for the manufacture of bricks. This whole depth concluded on a bed of chalky rubble and on this evidence it seems as though the strata of clay and brickearth lay above the native chalk. A closer examination revealed a seam of the ochreous flint nodules that were obviously deemed superfluous to the brickmaking process and fared little better as road material but here I am certain was the source of the crafted piece that had first caught my ankle and then my attention. As I picked at the face of the excavation I did not unearth another fashioned flint but instead what seemed like a large and weighty bone that was certainly animal in origin but I had neither the tools nor the time to continue with its investigation. With only the benefit of seventeen summers on this earth I do not know the answer to the mystery of how a piece of stone that appears to have been shaped by human design can be buried naturally at such a depth and to lie in combination with animal remains. These are indeed questions for a mind much greater than my own and perhaps I will in time, meet such a person if fate can but arrange it. I then left the brickyard with a vow that I should

return someday and study the curious strata in greater
detail and also to interview the workmen here to
establish whether the brickearth has yielded other
faunal remains which even the most unobservant
should surely recognise.

I struggled on for a good mile with my ankle now
burning and the sun which had been present
throughout this long day was now making its
departure with spectacular effect. Nothing was
deemed too lowly for the great wash of its golden
pigment; the grazing beast, an old gatepost and even
the tumbled down roadside cott seemed to relish the
final benevolence of the day.

I found no small surprise in the way that this small
town of Wilton had been given over to the weaving of
cloth and carpets. The innkeeper at the Bell inn, for
that is where I now write these pages, informs me that
as many as one thousand people are employed in this
trade. (I recall your wisdom that landlords are prone
to exaggeration so you can make your computations
accordingly.)

Certainly the air is thick with the smell of dyes
and the acrid stench of the fulling process. My

arrival at the Bell Inn near the market place was coincident with an incoming stage and I believe the landlord mistook me for a passenger as he enquired as to my comfort on the journey, for my part I felt in too much discomfort from my fall to correct him. I ate a modest supper of mutton, sitting at a table in the parlour with a couple from Somerset, Mr and Mrs William Handsome, who were irrepressible in their anticipation of a visit to Wilton House in the morning, Mr Andrew Staples, a clothier from Bath on business and Mr Nicholas Cowen, a very tall gentleman from I know not where who seemed to enjoy his pipe before, during and after the meal. I then retired to my room to begin this account of my first day as a pedestrian tourist and thankful for the speed that I am able to write, one blessing available to the simple clerk. I will bid you goodnight Dear Uncle but before I am able to sleep I intend to seek out the landlady to see if a little laudanum will relieve the painful throbbing in my ankle.

Your ever faithful Nephew and servant
HENRY CHALK

P.S. Having no notion of the hour but finding that I am caught somewhere between sleep and waking dreams I have relit the candle and again taken up my pen. My ankle pains me still even after the draught which only seems to have brought about wild and cataclysmic visions. I have been dreaming of great seas washing across a wild landscape and as tides recede, all at a furious pace, huge rivers converge to shift and scour the hillsides with alternating warmth and great coldness yet this seems like no biblical catastrophe presided over by an angry God, these are natural forces at work. I sense that these horrifying events are somehow of this place and have occurred at a junction of river valleys that are now gentle and subdued but it was not always so. Somewhere in this tumult I saw my flint nodule repeatedly turning through the air, cutting skin, flesh and sinew, the edges bloody, the nodule then falls into clear water the blood reeling away in pale red ribbons with the flow of the river until the silt blows across the stony bed and its shape is lost. I want to retrieve the piece from my pocket to see that it is not lost but my eyes are straining and I must close them.

Friday 9th October 1807

M Y D E A R U N C L E

I realise now how thoughtless I must appear having
not enquired after your health when I have selfishly
dedicated pages to my own circumstances, although
perhaps it is the nature of the traveller to be
absorbed so. As I write these words I am crouched in
a woodland clearing where a primitive of times
unrecorded would feel at home. Indeed it is as if I
have been thrown back into an age where the
luxuries of modern life have not yet even been
imagined. But I am jumping ahead of myself and
must begin the day at the Bell Inn when after
breakfast on reaching for my purse to pay for my
accommodation I found it not about my person. I
searched my pack and the room but to no avail. I can
think of only one circumstance when this loss could
have occurred and that was the event of my fall yesterday evening and more particularly the assistance

offered by the man and boy who so cheerfully helped me to my feet and it appears cheerfully helped themselves to my purse. Their hasty departure should have alerted me and the moment having passed I can only make a lesson of it for the future. I am again indebted to you my Dear Uncle for I followed your example of keeping safe a single guinea piece for just such a disaster.

Unwisely it seems, I confided in the landlord that my pocket had been picked the previous day which combined with the fall was ill luck for this pedestrian tourist. His already landlordish complexion grew more so until I produced the guinea piece, but he made it clear that that he was not disposed to pedestrian tourists and had he realised that I had not arrived aboard last evening's mail then no room would have been made available and he bid me a "Good marnin' young zur". However before departing I submitted yesterdays letter for posting and sought out the maid and tipped her one shilling as you instructed in your journal but "boots" was nowhere to be found and I spent his sixpence on a loaf of bread from the bakery in the town.

The streets were teaming with the comings and goings of those connected with the cloth and carpet industry, dyers with their overshirts flecked with every hue and wagons stacked high with woolsacks turning slowly at the crossroads. The broad burr of Wiltshire voices could be heard from the greetings and partings of workmen and gentlemen alike, much different to the harsher London tongue of which I must class my own speech. With my ankle swollen, but at this stage in a tolerable condition for slow walking, I made my way along West Street. I had already decided, after an earlier consultation with Mr Cary's map, to explore a tract of woodand called Grovelly and see whether autumn had yet taken a grip, with a desire to be free of the hustle and bustle of even this small town of Wilton as it puts in mind too much of aspects of London.

A pedestrian is able to pass through a tollgate without expense and has the pleasure of being able to walk on a good road for nothing. As I exchanged the time of day with the gatekeeper I wondered whether my simple form of travel would one day become an acceptable pursuit and so the landlord at the Bell Inn,

for the sake of his livelihood, would have to amend
this prejudice and welcome the pedestrian tourists. It
is certainly the best way to witness every passing
detail for as I climbed up towards the wood I was
amazed at the industry of the spiders here with their
webs binding the hedgerows, each delicate thread
glistening and sagging under the weight of the
morning dew. Flocks of birds I feel ashamed that I
cannot name were massing out on the stubble fields,
feeding on the remnants of the harvest until as one
they would turn their attentions to the wayside bushes
that glowed red with berries and squabble over these
until another charge is called and back to the fields
they go. I told myself that I had no right to be so full of
cheer as I hobbled on with the sun at my back and I
even began to sing aloud to the spiders and the
unnamed flocks. As I entered the shadows of Grovelly
my ankle again pained me greatly and I now followed
uneven woodland trails with many halts along the
way. At every turn grew regular clumps of the same
bush, these stunted trees had no one single trunk but
many straight shiny brown rods that looked ideally
suited to providing me with a walking support. I

launched into one of these trackside bushes and as I was in the act of twisting and thrashing one such pole in an attempt to detach it I heard a loud curse from behind me. I turned at once to find a small man whose skin was so darkened with grime that one may have mistaken him for a chimney sweep, although we were some distance from the nearest chimney. I could see by his agitation that he was not pleased by my actions although he might have been speaking another language as I could not comprehend a single word he uttered. I explained my own predicament but the little man appeared to be equally uncomprehending, I then hopped on my good leg until I eventually tumbled over and sat on the soft forest floor. The man grunted at my lame demonstration before setting down his large leather bag and from beneath his coat he produced a heavy hooked knife and with a few swift blows in the midst of the bush he extracted a stick with a fork at one end and a curious barley twist in the middle. I hauled myself to my feet and received the walking stick and it was indeed a handsome aid for any man with my thumb fitting perfectly into the cleft at the top. I thanked him and he nodded approvingly but did not stand aside to let me pass, instead he rubbed his thumb and forefinger together before my face. I was happy to pay for my new stick out of my diminished funds but in temporarily giving up my support to reach into my pocket I again lost my balance and returned to the forest floor but on this occasion I cried out in pain for I had tried to put weight on my weak ankle. The man from the woods gestured for me to remove my boot and stocking and the swelling was plain to see. He then gathered up my boot and stocking and slung his own bag across his shoulder and hauled me upright. Supporting me with a strong arm he indicated the direction we were to follow and although not of great stature I felt his immense strength as he guided me between the stunted bushes. His hands are large and blackened and have seen a lifetime of rough work and he has a strong odour of bonfires and soot about his person. After some labouring by my human support and some helplessness on my part we approached a clearing in the wood and the trade of my new acquaintance became apparent, he is a charcoal burner and all about lay evidence of his woodland craft.

My Dear uncle, I must now set down my pen for I have a curious duty to perform at the request of my host which in time I will describe.

Having now brought me to his camp I sensed that the little man was now ill at ease and knew not what to do with me. In the centre of the encampment was positioned a large smoking heap that I took to be charcoal in the making and he began the business of tidying and tending to his livelihood but would then falter and look about to where I sat observing his every action out of my own curiosity. In time a boy appeared of perhaps ten years of age who shared the same grimy countenance and viewed me with equal suspicion from across the woodland clearing. The charcoal burner now departed and the boy began a task of tying up bundles of small branches and stacking them aboard a cart. I could do little but take out my writing set and all was silence in the camp save for birdsong and the nearby rustlings of small woodland creatures. In time the master of the smouldering heap reappeared and in seeing me at my writing scurried away to his primitive hut and returned with a book which he took no time in pressing towards me. I took the volume and opened the cover and to my surprise I found it to be "Robinson Crusoe". The little man stabbed his short blackened finger at the illustration in the frontispiece of Robinson and his negro Friday on the shores of the desert island. It is a book that I read not a year ago and the story was still with me, so striking was the adventure and the telling of it. After my inspection I was for returning the book but the charcoal burner made it very apparent that he expected me to relate this tale to him on the spot with his face a picture of anticipation. Having no other tasks to perform with my ankle not permitting any further distance I put aside my pen and began to read aloud the tale of "Robinson Crusoe". I had not read more than a single page when this small mans dirty and furrowed brow knitted together as it had when we first met and I knew this to be a clear indication of his dissatisfaction. I gathered that he was not comprehending the words or language or even my own unfamiliar speech and so I began to recite slower and with more plainness but still the man grew restless. As the story was fresh in my mind I decided to take a different action and make a simpler model and even a drama of it as best I could. With the volume in my left hand to remind me of the order of the tale and importantly I believed to give the impression of recitation from the book to its unlikely owner and so I began.

My Dear Uncle, you will well remember the tale yourself and I shall not repeat it here save for the moments when I judged the success of my dramatics by the interest on the faces of my audience of two, for the boy had now abandoned his work to stand open mouthed beside his master. After leaving Hull, Robinson first encounters the full force of the sea and sorely regrets his actions and for not heeding his Fathers pleas to remain at home. Of the severe storm at Yarmouth when the ship is at anchor and the captain prays with the crew for their very lives and they are saved while the ship flounders. You will well imagine my actions of wind, storm and boiling seas for the more I made of it the wider grew the eyes of man and boy. How long I continued in this manner I do not know until I required a rest from it and placed a fallen leaf between the paper leaves to keep place

and closed the book. Both were vocal in their
resistance to this halt in the proceedings but I
explained that it could not be done at one sitting and
there were many pages to follow and a fellow must
keep his strength up by eating and drinking. I shared
with my new companions my bread, cheese and ham
and with little hesitation they devoured all my carried
provisions offering me in return a hard, flat and
tasteless substance that I believe is called "barley
bannock". They also drank deeply from an old flagon
to which I politely refused lest it was beer which I
cannot abide even the smell of, preferring instead the
water from my own flask.

There is now an opportunity while the
smouldering heap receives further attention with the
careful adjustment of the surrounding lattice wooden
panels that screen an almost imperceptible wind from
affecting this slow conflagration and in this interval I
can again take up my pen. I would dearly like to be
able to give some account of the language of these
people for the man has I sense an impediment to his
speech where he cannot make a word without forming
a straining from his nose which is an affliction that

must have caused him great difficulty for all of his life. The boy though appears to understand his masters every command whilst he himself is all "burrs" and "aarhs" as I find customary here in South Wiltshire, with words that I can hear but do not always comprehend for there must be a local vocabulary. I sense that I will be required shortly to resume the tale of Robinson Crusoe and I cannot disguise my enjoyment of this role and the effects that my words and actions are bringing to these Wiltshire faces. I should also like, if the opportunity permits, to try out my skills with my pencil to see if I can capture this woodland scene for it is filled with interest and there is a tidiness and order here that belies the appearance of its blackened occupants. I find myself of a sudden in a strangers world and I can do little to affect the situation and I know not where I shall sleep this very night for I cannot leave even if I wish it, which I do not, and I am content to open my eyes and mind and become myself a part of this place.

Having just eaten the most greasiest of stews, I can now report My Dear Uncle, that I am no longer in the heart of Grovelly wood but that I have been

installed in the lowliest of inns which makes the Bell
Inn   at   Wilton   appear   a   most   respectable
establishment. As dusk began to creep in amongst the
trees the charcoal burner signalled that I must leave
the woods and at first I did not know to what
destination. I then departed with the boy aboard a
horse and cart on a journey along woodland tracks. As
we rattled along I established that the boys name is
Tam and his master's name is Peter Winter. I told him
my name and from thereon he refered to me as
"Master 'Enry". There were strange hootings that Tam
explained as being "a nowl" and he mimicked this
earie sound exactly causing great confusion with the
originator of the call and, I suspect, with any other
nowls in the district. In time we emerged into open
country with the great wood at our backs. The evening
was cold and clear and the sinking sun made a great
blood red mess above the distant tree cloaked hills
across the valley with the clouds all scratched and
torn about. Interrupting the far horizon I noted a
structure, perhaps a spire or tower that must be of
some considerable height to announce its presence
from such a distance. When asked to identify this

curiosity Tam shrugged his shoulders and then whistled merrily until we reached our destination, a low building beside a trackway with blue woodsmoke creeping up pencil straight from its chimney. Before I could climb down from the cart Tam had already entered the place and explained my circumstances to the landlord. An old board on the face of the building named this establishment "The New Inn" which I could just read in the failing light and it is indeed not a new inn at all. After a consultation with Mr Cary's map I see that its position is recorded to the south of Grovelly wood and as a consequence I now have some idea of the position of Peter Winters camp. Tam unloaded the "vaggits" of bundled wood that he had prepared earlier and was soon departing back up the track "Boi master 'Enry, oil zee thee n' the marnin'"

My accommodation takes the form of a small loft, situated directly above the parlour and it was with great difficulty that I negotiated the vertical ladder with my ankle still painful and weak. The loft has a narrow cot on one side and a shuttered window on the other and through the gaps in the bare boards I could see the activity below in the parlour. Supper was

served in this room below and I have already
remarked as to its content. I sat at the only table in
the place and around the walls sat men on benches
dressed in long overshirts with pots of ale in hand,
fuming on long clay pipes which they had jammed
between their whiskers. I gauged that my presence in
this building was a source of great amusement, sat as
I was in my London clothes, for there were many nods
and glances in my direction from these fellows and
some laughter also. I judged that this place was like a
stable, not for horses but for rough countrymen and
workers of the land for there was straw spread about
the floor and it mingled with the mud from these
working men's boots. After the completion of my meal
I knew not what to do other than to retire to my loft for
the night and again take up my pen. I am sitting upon
the course grey blankets of my cot and I hold a great
apprehension as to what I might find between them
when I muster the courage to lay down for the night. I
have spied a small hole in the roof tiles that frames a
bright half moon and there is a growing coldness in
this place to which I am bracing myself for a
desperate night. I recall from earlier in the day the

tale of Robinson Crusoe who regretted on many
occasions the loss of his family and home and that
steady middle ground through life that his father did
his utmost to guide him towards rather than the peaks
and troughs of adventure. As you are only too aware
Sir my parents are no longer of this earth yet I could
still take that middle ground that my Father, your
Brother, would have dearly wished for me.

I shall now prepare for bed and wish you a goodnight
my Dear Uncle in the hope that you will not tire of the
accounts of my deeds as I fear there is no other
possible recipient for my scribbles.

Your faithful and errant Nephew
HENRY CHALK

P.S. I fear that I must test your patience further
with this postscript.

I have in my hand your own publication of "A Tour
of North Wales 1805" which has greatly informed and
inspired in equal measure. I refer to your comments
on the essential preparations required for such an
excursion, and an item that you consider
indispensable, "a crisply starched white nightshirt".

As always I have followed your advice with strict attention and having dressed for bed I stood holding the candle before me and looked about the place and also down at myself. Here I am in this damp and dirty loft, in this world where whiteness plays no part, enveloped in rank tobacco smoke from the parlour below and about to enter between grey and filthy bedding. I can inform you that I am standing in my nightshirt, shining as brightly as if I were a visitation of the Angel Gabriel himself. I sincerely intend no blasphemy sir, but it is a situation that has warmed my heart and brought me no small amusement, for which I thank you.

The Charcoal Burner

The New Inn

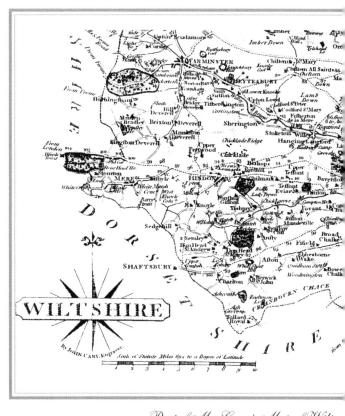

Part of Mr. Cary's Map of Wilt-

shire, shewing the Southern Parts thereof

Flint Nodule
Stourton

Gunflint
Grovelly Pit

Flint Butchery Tool
Fisherton Brickearth

☞ *These sketches are made at two-thirds actual size*

Saturday 10th October 1807

MY DEAR UNCLE,

I awoke before day break with the crowing of a
cockerel in the yard and dogs barking also. In the
night I dressed myself in my day clothes and returned
to bed in the hope that I might become warmer but if
I am to stay another night here I will demand more of
these filthy blankets. After hearing movement
downstairs and the crackling of a new fire in the grate
I arose and descended carefully with my ankle not yet
repaired and warmed myself for some minutes before
the blaze. Presently I drew a pail of cold water from
the well and carried out my ablutions as best I could
and I am still required to use my new stick for even
these smallest of tasks. There has been no indication
of how I should break my fast although I can report
that I have drunk a cup of milk that was still warm
from the brown cow that appears to wander freely
here. At first I thought it content to browse from the

hedges and eat whatever grass exists beside the muddy track although as the boy heaved the hay down from the loft above the stable, the beast has grown wise to this event and now feasts contentedly on the horse's breakfast. The chickens are picking and scratching out on the track below my window and here comes "cock-a-doodle-do" who has just trampled on the back of one poor bird, to which she took great offence in clucking noisily and flustering her feathers back into order. The stable boy has now spied the antics of the brown cow and has slapped its rump to drive it away from the stable door with a loud curse. Observing life from the open shutters of my loft here at the "New Inn" is not without interest but I should like to be reunited with Peter Winter and the boy Tam as I feel a kinship growing which I cannot readily explain. I am curious also as to how a simple woodsman can possess a book that he can never hope to read yet he appears to derive some pleasure from my foolish rendition. I believe it is a grave mistake to under-estimate any man for they are always sure to surprise.

I am now sitting near the smouldering heap in Peter Winters' camp for Tam was true to his word and

appeared at the "New Inn " to fill up the water barrel
on his cart from the well and we slowly rolled back up
into the shadows of Grovelly with the water slapping
against the insides of the barrel. Tam has informed
me that his Mother's sister is the landlady of that inn
to which he supplies the "vaggits" of bound wood in
return for milk and eggs. In a blackened bowl I have
just eaten a meal of "mushroons n' cheddies" of
which the former are gathered from the fields nearby
and the latter is but the simple potato. It was a
warming dish if not providing much taste to the palate
and I was thankful for it. I was fully prepared to read
aloud Peter's book but both he and Tam are busy at
their tasks. The boy is sat with a heavy hooked knife
cutting these walking stick poles along their lengths
to produce bundles of these "zpars" as he has named
them. Tam then made the shape of a roof with his
hands to indicate their purpose and perhaps they are
used to affix the shaggy straw that is so common
hereabouts.

I have a series of small bites about my skin which
I can only attribute to those "dancing legions of the
night" to which you so eloquently refer on your travels

in North Wales. I can confirm that they also abide in great number at the "New Inn". Peter has gestured for me to join him aboard the horse and cart and I shall not keep him waiting.

Our destination was unclear, but I was content to observe the many activities that take place within this great wood. There are a minority of other charcoal burners at large here with their own smouldering heaps and some that have reached an advanced stage of production where the finished charcoal has cooled sufficiently for it to be exported from the wood. I saw no heaps as yet unburned and I am wondering that the charcoal burning season in Grovelly is almost at an end. It appears that charcoal production is not the primary task of these woodsmen for their skills are many and indeed the woven panels are stacked high in these clearings and must be in great demand as pens and fences. There is one industry here of which I cannot establish a purpose and that is the stripping of bark from certain trees and it appears as though it is the bark itself that is the important commodity and not the timber. This bark is then loaded high in great wagons and taken I know not where and it is on these occasions that my inability to understand Peter Winter's grunted explanations that frustrates. We passed a wooden hut that was fully draped with the dead carcasses of birds and small mammals and on this occasion we halted. Peter then took a bulging sack from our cart and emptied it at the feet of the occupant of this morbid dwelling and amongst this pile of unfortunate creatures were a number of the red bushy tailed tree rats that I had watched with great fascination during my short time within this wood. In a flash from their position on the ground they could ascend to any position and pass from branch to branch and tree to tree as swiftly as any bird on the wing. A count was now made of all these limp and lifeless corpses and with some form of agreement settled upon we were again on our way.

At the far edge of the wood, where a long ditch seems to mark the boundary between Grovelly and the outside world, we again halted and Peter gestured for me to disembark also. He then took a digging tool and entered a deep pit and I observed from above his hacking and scraping at the ground. From this thick reddish brown soil Peter prized out a number of large irregular flints which he then hurled in my direction. I did not realise his purpose as he sat down on a timber out of the shadow of the wood and from the bottomless pocket of his black coat he withdrew a small hammer wrapped in a piece of course leather. He then draped the leather across his lap and began striking these nodules with the hammer. I sat down beside Peter Winter and noted that he was smiling to himself, seemingly enjoying the mystery and knowing now my curiosity and hunger for explanation. With sharp taps of his hammer he first quartered the blocks and I could see how the leather was required for protection against this action. With further deft blows and with a great speed that he employs in all his activities, the pieces were reduced further until they resembled the size and form of a segment of an orange. Peter then turned his hammer to utilise the pointed end and struck a careful blow to this segment, detaching a small flint wedge which he then held up for my inspection. To emphasize its purpose he mimed the aiming and firing of a gun and then laughed whilst I acknowledged that I now understood that his many skills extended to the production of gunflints. This, apparently, was not the finished article as there was further trimming required but for now Peter dropped the piece into a bag and the spent orange segment was tossed to the ground. I now realised my part in this procedure as Peter again reached into his coat pocket and produced Robinson Crusoe and I had for competition the splitting of flint ringing about my ears.

There was a further distraction happening in the open field where a gang of labourers was digging a great pit from which cart loads of fresh white chalk were being extracted and spread about the surface of this field. The rich brown clay soil, the same as was clinging to Peter's flint nodules, had been drawn to the sides to gain access to the underlying chalk and I would have dearly liked an explanation on this matter. Peter simply shrugged when asked, as if what went on beyond the bounds of Grovelly was of little concern to him. The sight of this bright white substance in the morning sun took my mind further away from the desert island and to the instance of the digging of the great well in the brewery yard in Southall. It is perhaps the occasion of the last contact between us Sir before this current flood of

correspondence and you will recall, at that time, my
eager anticipation of this project for it was indeed
undertaken at my suggestion. You will I hope forgive
me, My Dear Uncle, if I now inform you of the
circumstances of the digging of the great well as it
preys on my mind often for it was completed shortly
before the death of my Father, and your Brother. I
somehow believe that it is chalk that has guided my
destiny and it is perhaps a quest for chalk that has
brought me here to Wiltshire. You will I gauge believe
these to be foolish words from a foolish youth but
please, I pray, firstly let me attempt to justify these
words and my actions by explanation.

I believe I told you of the contamination suffered
to the water at the brewery from the old shallow well
and the need to somehow remedy the situation. On my
visits to the British Musem Library I found a
publication by the Board of Agriculture relating in
part to the digging of wells and I proposed this to my
father as a solution. I warned of the great depth that
would be necessary, perhaps as much as six hundred
feet, and I made calculations as to the cost of
materials and labour and these he then presented to

the bank. It was surely a great investment as no other brewery in London would have such a fine source of water and beer is not a commodity that will decline in its public demand. The bank deemed it a sound proposal and work commenced immediately. Two men were employed to the task and cart upon cart load of London bricks were required to line the well and mountains of spoil were drawn up and hauled away from this core into the earth beneath London. At any opportunity I would leave my desk to observe the changing nature of this extracted material as it appeared, with month upon month of sand, gravel and clay. Despite my calculations as to the depth and cost of this operation my Father became more agitated with every passing week and would then scold me for suggesting such a venture. I recall the afternoon when my Father was on a visit to the bank and I was able to stare from the office window and noted how the spoil had changed from a pale clay slop to great pure white lumps of chalk and of a sudden this brightness made the yard an exceedingly dull and dirty place. I ran down the steps to inspect this magic white material, tipping out the buckets and pushing around in the heap and I cared not that my hands, boots and clothes became white in an instant. It was at this moment that my Father, your Brother, returned to the brewery with a representative from the bank to assess the progress of the investment. I shall not forget the look on my Father's face if I live to be one hundred years, to find his only son and heir at play in a spoil heap, covered from top to toe in chalk dust when he should have been working at his desk. As my Father trembled with rage the gentleman from the bank merely shook his head as if he were witnessing the antics of a simpleton and said; "In name and nature, Master Chalk". I will not recount the extent of my punishment save to say that no effort was spared, with the lesson that I must be fixed in my ambition to one day be the owner of a fine brewery and not a simple labourer. I was also forbidden my weekly visit to the British Museum Library which pained me more that any beating. As the weeks passed My Father only addressed me on matters of business where my duties as a clerk demanded his attention and I dared not go near the well, even in his absence, least I should get a speck of this chalk on my clothes or shoes.

You will imagine my frustrations when water was finally reached. At first there were raised voices of alarm as the excavator of the well signalled that he should be drawn up at once and it was feared that he would be drowned in the cradle such was the ferocity of the water emerging from the deep. In only three hours the water rose to more than three hundred feet and over the next two days it rose one foot in the hour. The relief on my Father's face was palpable as his deepening investment finally bore its rewards and Chalks beer could now finally be renowned for its purity above all other London breweries. At no time did he give any recognition that it had been my idea or did he permit me to join the cheering and celebration in the yard.

If my handwriting trembles it is not through the telling of this tale but of the cold here at the "New Inn". The candlelight flickers in the gentle night breeze as there is little to halt its progress as it passes through this building.

I must return to the travails of the one legged pedestrian tourist as I left him near the dank flint pit with Robinson Crusoe in hand if not in mind. Whilst

Peter Winter filled his bag with gunflints I did my
best with the book but was sorely distracted by the
activity before me, the piles of chalk in the field and
my own wandering thoughts. At one time I put my
hand in my coat pocket and felt the fashioned flint
from the brickearth pit near Salisbury. I pulled it
out, half in the hope that it might draw Peter's
attention away from the activities of the castaway
which indeed it did. He demanded to view it and
turned it around slowly in his hand, the dark brows
converged as the storm clouds gathered but not in
anger or frustration on this occasion, only I believe,
out of curiosity. I carefully relayed the details of its
provenance,   not   knowing   how   much   of   this
information would interest the charcoal burner. All
the while he turned it around in his hand and held it
for a moment between thumb and forefinger then
moving it from side to side. In an instant he was back
in the pit and returned having prized out another flint
nodule. He then embarked on the same reduction
process as before but on this occasion he stopped
short of reaching the orange segment and instead
worked on a larger, flatter piece. One attempt was

flung to the ground with a loud grunt but the second proved more successful and he then worked around the circumference of the shape, striking small shards of flint from both faces. Whilst Peter was engaged in this work I hobbled about to get the blood moving in my limbs. Littering the soil all around the pit amongst the autumn stubble were the discarded orange segments from previous gun flint manufacture. Some were as dark and fresh looking as those of today yet many were clouded, perhaps affected by weather and the passing of time. These may be the residue of gunflint workers from earlier generations and I do not know how long it takes for broken flint to turn from dark to cloudy. Peter held up the finished piece for my inspection and immediately returned to his gunflints as if enough time had been wasted already. It was slightly smaller than my original but cleverly made and fiercely sharp. He snatched it back and easily cut through the corner of his leather protector to prove its efficiency. He smiled at the success of his craftsmanship and then returned it with a nod towards Robinson Crusoe to which I could only agree to oblige.

I feel that as long as I keep the pen in my hand I will not have to enter between those dreaded blankets but I sense a heaviness in my eyelids. I must relate also that from our position at the edge of Grovelly wood near the flint pit and beyond where the workers dug into the field, lay in the distance a great tract of land that Mr Cary's map confirms as Salisbury Plain. It is an open vista on such a grand scale that I have never before witnessed and when my ankle is repaired, and it feels better with each passing day, I shall set my coat tails and enter upon its gently rolling surface in search of that lost island they call Stonehenge. I believe, my Dear Uncle, that Mr Robinson Crusoe has greatly affected my mind for I now see water where there is only land. Sir, I bid you a cold and scratchy goodnight.

Your Faithful Nephew
HENRY CHALK

MY DEAR UNCLE,

I have cabin fever for I am confined to the environs of the "New Inn". Tam again kindly returned me to my lodgings here last evening yet as we parted I recall now that he made no reference to a meeting today. It is after all the Lord's Day but without my woodland friends time passes slowly. I have hobbled about this place observing the occasional passer-by and I feel like some wayside simpleton who has no other task to perform. I have drawn this building as it is not without interest as a simple establishment but the light is poor and there has been rain with the clouds as grey and dirty as the blankets in my loft.

I can report Sir that last night did not pass without some drama and surprise. The parlour was full of noise and rising tobacco smoke which did choke me and after attempting sleep I resolved to remove to the hay loft above the stables where I gauged I may have a

warmer and more peaceful slumber. I know not at
what hour but I was awoken at first by dogs barking
and then by voices in the empty stall below. In a
lamp's light I observed two men, who were earlier this
very evening in the parlour and indeed were now
heavily influenced by liquor, as they struggled
between them with the carcass of a large deer. With
one end of a rope attached to its hind legs, the other
was then cast over a beam and with great exertion the
two men eventually managed to raise and suspend
upside down the unfortunate beast. The stable door
was closed yet evidently with a third character
outside on the track keeping watch. There then began
a display of intoxicated butchery which my eyes were
drawn to observe for not being one to turn from the
sight of such things. With a freshly whetted blade, the
first man, who had now removed his long shirt and
under shirt, placed the horses' water bucket beneath
the animals head and then slit its throat. As the pail
filled with the steady flow of thick dark red blood he
stood back and the two men passed a flagon between
them. The butcher then returned to the task and made
a deep incision into the belly of the beast with the

second character stood behind the carcass to hold it as steady as a drunken man was able. The three-quarter full pail was removed and the first man, with his bare hands, began to scoop out the innards onto the straw below and of a sudden there was a bang on the stable door. The lamp was fumbled for by the second man who in doing so released the deer to swing forward and strike the butcher who already had his hands full with knife and entrails who then tumbled over backwards to the floor. The voice from outside reassured the two men that all was well and there followed a succession of curses from inside the stable that I could neither fully understand nor wish to repeat. In summary however it was agreed that "stoopid Mart'n ee did vall azleep agin' thik dur". The animal was then crudely skinned and the apportioning of the meat began. At one stage I sensed that I would sneeze from the dust in the hayloft but I kept as silent as I could for fear of discovery as I knew not what these dangerous and drunken men would do to me if they but realised that there was a witness to their criminality. My Dear uncle I only relate this event to you in the strictest confidence for as I was

contemplating on the penalties that would befall
these deer stealers if apprehended, I felt a chill at the
mention of a name known to me. It was evident that
these characters were to meet young Tam at a
prearranged location, to only one end that I could
perceive, and that was the passing on of illicit meat.
One parcel of venison was concealed in a dark corner
of the stable and I began to suspect that everyone
from the landlord to the stable boy was to benefit from
the oversight of this night-time butchery. Even the
dogs here at the "New Inn" were complicit in
removing the evidence as they were finally let in to
clean up the entrails from where they lay in the straw.
The men departed and I heard a cart draw way. I
wondered at my own position, should I attempt to
return to my bed and perhaps alarm the household or
should I remain in the stable and risk detection in the
morning? I must have spent too long considering this
issue for the next I knew the stable boy had thrown
open the doors of the hay loft and I awoke to see the
surprise on his face and his readiness to pierce me
with the long fork. I explained to the boy that I could
not sleep in the Inn for it was too noisy and that I had

had a very comfortable and warm nights rest. The stable boy viewed me with caution as I could not have failed to witness the proceedings during the night. The Landlord beckoned me as I was at the well and asked if I had "Zlept good?". He is a nervous man with a quick eye and a strong odour of onions about his person. I replied that I had never slept better, which was indeed true, and that this evening I would be looking forward to a hearty meal. At my response the Landlord smiled weakly and retreated swiftly from whence he came. Perhaps I am playing a dangerous game but I feel that it is very much in the spirit of this place and I have received enough thin and greasy stews to date.

Indeed my words to the Landlord did not go unheeded for when I sat at my table in the empty parlour, my greasy stew was supplemented by a moderate portion of the illicit meat. The cook had somehow contrived a toughness that gave considerable exercise to the jaw and teeth but I welcomed the challenge nevertheless. I had barely pushed aside my plate when there was a knock at the door to which the Landlord feigned some alarm. It was apparently a visit from the Parish Constable who took a deliberate look about the place to ensure that the sanctity of the Lord's Day was being observed. Having satisfied himself in this respect he then confirmed with the Landlord that I was indeed a guest and was therefore entitled to enjoy the custom at the "New Inn" on this day. After clearing his throat this lean gentleman, who did not wear the ubiquitous embroidered overshirt but instead a simple black coat, then presented himself before the solitary table to address me in person. "Zur, gent'man zur" began the Constable, "You wud be the gent'man zur thas been abroad n' the wud zur?". I introduced myself and explained my purpose as a pedestrian tourist and my predicament also, having taken a fall and was therefore resting until sufficiently recovered to continue. This information was greeted with the blankest of blank expressions. " Yus zur, n' I spec youm be makin' yur way presently, beggin' yur pardon zur." I could only imagine that this apparent contrivance had been at the initiation of the sly Landlord as he had not the wit to be discreet in his surprise and simply nodded his agreement to the parish official's every word. I informed both gentlemen that I would indeed be departing in the morning and I felt that there was little to be gained from any form of protest. I do feel, My Dear Uncle, that I shall be able to make some slow progress tomorrow and it will be a relief to vacate the "New Inn". Having carried out his duty the Parish Constable was then invited to stay for a pot of beer, to which he feigned persuasion, whilst I excused myself to take the air outside in the lane before I retired. I shall lay fully clothed on my cot for this my final slumber as I do not wish to provide easy nourishment for those "dancing legions of the night". In the parlour below I can still hear the low rumble of conversation and through the gap in the floorboards I have witnessed the Landlord presenting the Parish Constable with a small package which he quickly secreted in his coat pocket.

I would like to make acquaintance again with Peter Winter and the boy Tam before I depart from Grovelly. I shall have to forsake Robinson Crusoe, marooned still on his desert island but I do not feel that the charcoal burner is concerned with the book's completion. He requests over again the same passages; the shipwreck, the discovery of Man Friday and any episodes with the firing of muskets and the hunting of fowl or game.

I shall now bid you a goodnight and I hope tomorrow to be able to post the accumulated pages of correspondence that will, I fear, now arrive in one large flood rather than a steady trickle.

Your faithful and repaired Nephew
HENRY CHALK

Monday morning 12th October 1807

SIR it is now the following morning and I have a little time available before sealing my correspondence and I shall therefore continue whilst I can. Tam arrived at the "New Inn" with a cart load of "vaggits" first thing and kindly transported me to Peter Winter's camp in Grovelly as I desired. You will not be surprised to learn Sir that neither he nor I made reference to the activities late on Saturday night. He will depart shortly to Wilton where he has agreed to meet the post. I opened my shutters at daybreak to witness a pack of hounds as they made their approach to the inn led by their Master and another gentleman, dressed for the business in hand in their scarlet hunting jackets. The Landlord brought out two pots of ale for these gentlemen who remained mounted whilst the steaming dogs with their tails wagging descended into the murky pond that lies to the side of that place. The Master, on his necessarily large steed, was cursing loudly a gentleman called Mr Beckford who would not it seems permit hunting on his land. "If the abominable fellow would only let us across his acres we'd have a straight run through to Wardour" (I know not whether this spelling is correct) The second gentleman then speculated on how many foxes found safe harbour in this forbidden territory and they both drained their pots with a grimace and a curse at the sourness of the ale. The Master blew his horn and the whole noisy affair continued on its way with the pack responding with yelps of pleasure at their morning exercise. I then settled up with the obsequious Landlord and felt under no obligation to leave a tip with a promise to myself never to return to that place.

We did not proceed on our usual route into Grovelly but instead we continued along the trackway to the south of the woodland for some distance. In time at a crossing of the tracks and where a milestone was situated we turned and began our slow climb, for every way into the wood requires an ascent. Before the fringe of woodland was reached, Tam instructed the horse to halt and he jumped down and carried with him a woven basket. At first I could not see his purpose until, amongst the longer tufts of grass, he plucked out a number of the field fruits called mushroons and laid them in his basket. I joined him in this task and he indicated which were desirable. The best have a flat creamy top with their undersides a flesh pink and they have a freshness in smell that makes the juices run in the mouth. Tam picked more than could possibly be eaten at one sitting and he informed me that he transports them to Wilton where he has some demand there. As we moved from tuft to tuft I noted that there were many rabbit throws across this open grassland and amongst these black soil heaps lay a quantity of broken pottery pieces. I indicated   as   much   to   Tam   who   calls   them "panshards" and I pocketed an assortment and in addition I collected also some small coinage which when scraped clean has a silver appearance. Once I had established these signs of former occupation I recognised that there were many banks, hollows and sub-divisions all across these slopes on this southern aspect. It is an area that Tam refers to as "Amshill".

As Peter Winter returns to the camp from viewing his traps, so Tam can now depart to Wilton, for there must always be one of the pair in attendance to safeguard the smouldering heap least it should misbehave. I must seal my letter and bid you good morning My Dear Uncle. I fear my ink runs low and my well is near dry.

Monday afternoon 12th October 1807

My Dear Uncle,

I am on the move once more. My walking companion is my thumbstick and the stimulation of thought and slow pedestrianism is the perfect pace to view and ponder. My ankle is tolerable and today I have walked the farthest yet since my first shaky steps in this county. I have had many halts along the way but it suits me so as there is no urgency to my ramble and it will take more days yet before I am fully repaired. I am careful where I place my feet least I should turn my ankle again which would be nothing short of a disaster. Peter Winter has shown me how I should strap it up to walk and I shall repeat this method until I feel no discomfort and it is strong once more.

If the Landlord of the Bell Inn at Wilton felt ill disposed towards this pedestrian tourist when I was at my cleanest and least travel worn, I feared how I should be received at the respectable Deptford Inn now with the grime and aromas of Peter Winter's conflagrations strongly about my person. My duration at the New Inn did little to preserve a tidy appearance having slept in my day clothes for three nights and not once meeting with hot water. All was strangely silent when I made my approach to the inn yet I need not have reached such a state of apprehension as I was warmly greeted, the landlord and landlady being kindly and I believe they show a respect for all, gentlemen and common workmen alike. I have located "Boots" and requested a bath in my room and whilst this is being attended to I have taken up my pen in the parlour now that I have obtained a fresh supply of ink from the landlord. It is a pleasure to be sitting at a table and chair after days of crouching in Grovelly wood, furniture not being a necessity to the life of a charcoal burner there being only rough stools and stumps for the purpose of sitting down.

I did not leave Peter Winter's camp until late into the morning and I was pleased that he chose to walk with me for an hour or more. As Tam returned from Wilton and so we could now depart. I said a fond farewell to the boy Tam for I should have dearly liked to instruct him more in reading and writing. I wished to warn him also of the dangers of complicity in deer stealing with a great fear that one day he may get apprehended, but it is a consequence of making an existence here of which, as a Londoner, I can know but little nor pass judgement over. When the smouldering heap finally grows cold perhaps that will signal a departure from this place to endure a long and barren winter until their season begins over again and with Grovelly comes opportunity.

Peter seemed as glad as I to skirt the fringe of the wood and as I have now become accustomed he spoke little and kindly tempered his ferocious pace. We now witnessed the first signs of natures slow decline towards winter with the rattle of dry leaves and a trace of ice in the wind. A conspicuous and noisy bird then crossed our path which displayed a most impressive variety of coloured feathers with a white ring around its neck and a long tail and I believed it to be some form of exotic chicken. Peter mimed the aiming and firing of a gun and then cupped his hand to his ear and indeed we could hear distant cracks of gunfire and my guide then indicated that this strange bird was the intended quarry for this form of hunting. I did not wish to disturb the creature into flight lest it should head towards the battery of firing guns and certain death whilst the charcoal burner observed my attempted stealth with obvious amusement. As always Peter has a purpose to his actions and in time he led me to yet more signs of ancient occupation but this time on the northern side of the wood where great ditches and banks have been laid out on these ranging slopes, and from this position there is a tremendous aspect looking both up and down the valley and across to Salisbury Plain. I gauged that from their scale these must be defensive structures and yet they do not appear to form a complete circuit as I believed was customary. Our inspection revealed many more undulations continuing around the hill and indeed into the wood itself and again, as in the rabbit throws at Amshill, there are many small coins lying together with broken pottery. Earlier I had shown Peter the "panshards" from Amshill that I had collected this morning with the mushroons and I thought him little interested. Again I am at fault in my estimations as the Charcoal Burner now swept his arm across this area to suggest that if it was broken pottery and small soil encrusted coins that I desired then I was not to go wanting here. I have tried to establish the objects on this currency and there is I believe a head on one side and it is perhaps a galloping horse on the reverse. That these ancient peoples who made their settlements on both sides of this ridge lived in an age of metal there can be no doubt. If coins can be forged then tools and weaponry can be manufactured. Metal though cannot be extracted from chalk or flint so metal must be obtained from other regions for this purpose whereupon the elements of trade and transportation must be negotiated which are considered to be modern practices and not the activities of the barbarous savage. The habitations in this area are of grand proportions perhaps on the scale of a small town when combined with Amshill and its defences reveal a fear and vulnerability from the north. Indeed there are further indications of this insecurity with a ringed entrenchment that I have also visited today further west along the ridge, named "Castle" on John

Cary's map and also "Badbury Camp" which is situated on the downs above the small village of Wylye. I believe Sir, that this ridge was once a frontier, though who was feared and which battles were won and lost I cannot judge.

I have just heard a distant horn signalling an approaching stage and of a sudden the quiet here is broken with the bustle of preparation; the grooms busying themselves in the yard and the maids a' clattering in the kitchen. I wonder that my bath has been forgotten as until now this place has been asleep but I shall continue with my pen until I am disturbed by new arrivals or my appointment with hot water is due.

After our foraging for coins and broken pots my friend and guide indicated that he was to return to his camp and for a moment the tempestuous brow that I had feared at our first meeting cleared itself of all deep furrows and Peter Winter smiled. It was a brief affair that passed over like the weather on this October day, with a flash of sunlight between a flotilla of dark and heavy bottomed cloud. The charcoal burner, with a mischievous glint in his eye then tapped my hand as it clasped the handle of the walking stick and gave a quick rub of his thumb and forefinger to remind me that I had not yet paid him for his handiwork. There was so much that I should like to reimburse Peter for; his hospitality and kindness, the instruction in woodland craft and flintworking, his local wisdom and a deal more besides. I had not enough for all these things and I emptied my pocket of all coins into my cupped hand and this miserable pile of copper and silver was now all that I had left. I had given Tam a shilling this morning for the price of the postage of the letter and instructed him to keep the remainder. Peter grunted and picked out a sixpence from the pile in my hand for his stick and then turned without ceremony and quickly vanished into the wood. I wondered whether I would ever have the good fortune of meeting Peter Winter again yet I believe such is the way with travelling, brief relationships are made and then left behind but with a memory here that I shall always cherish in my heart. I am now sat up in my bed here in the Deptford Inn with a candle that sputters and spits and I see that I have wax on the page. I have a very interesting encounter to relate to you my Dear Uncle, with my bath awaiting, I was finishing the account of my departure from Grovelly wood when the passengers from the newly arrived coach filed through the parlour. First to show were two smart and fashionable young ladies who I now understand to be twins although their identical appearance suggested as much on my first impression and they were travelling with their chaperone. In close pursuit were two gentlemen who I also correctly gauged were father and son such were their facial similarities. Instinctively I ceased my labours with the pen and stood as the ladies entered and extended this courtesy to the two gentlemen. The elder of the two gentlemen, and the last in the line, then stopped and bid me "Good evening". He smiled and studied me more closely as I stood with pen in hand and I felt obliged to comment on the wretched sight that stood before him. "Good evening Sir. Please excuse my appearance I am a pedestrian tourist engaged on a short tour of the south of this county and I can inform you that I am due a bath very shortly".

"Indeed" He replied "I have met with pedestrian tourists before but never one who travels under the guise of a chimney sweeps boy. I am afraid Sir that I will not have our paths cross without discourse and explanation on this matter and I would therefore like to extend an invitation for you to join my son and me at dinner when I am certain that every part of this conundrum can be satisfactorily resolved". As you will know my funds have diminished to the extent of expecting only the most simple of meals and I did not wish to put upon a stranger or cause embarrassment to myself or another and so I politely declined with an explanation that I had already made my arrangements with the Landlord. The gentleman was not easily dissuaded but finally we agreed that once stomachs had been satiated I should be very welcome to join them. I can inform you that the gentleman's name is Mr Richard Fenton and he is travelling with his son Mr John Fenton. The gentleman then departed with a smile and a farewell gesture "I bid you a good evening and wish you an enjoyable repast, Mr Henry Chalk, Pedestrian Tourist." My ablutions were undertaken in barely three inches of cold water and I am gratified that I should feel no guilt when I leave this place without a tip for "Boots" for I have found him tardy and surly in his manner towards me. He is a young man yet older than myself and I suspect a degree of contempt in perhaps serving one younger than he and I have witnessed his ingratiating manner towards others. I shall also clean my own boots and dispense with his service entirely.

After my meal, which although simple was a veritable feast to one who has suffered the hospitality of the New Inn, the Landlord approached my table and asked whether I would now like to join the two gentlemen in the front room. More introductions were required for the benefit of Mr John Fenton and myself and before I had even become seated the same gentleman had pressed a large glass of wine into my hand and a toast was loudly proclaimed; "To Mr Henry Chalk, pedestrian tourist and no longer a chimney sweeps boy". On the insistence of these two irrepressible gentlemen I now gave a full account of my journey thus far although I refrained from relating the encounter with the pickpockets outside the brickyard near Salisbury as I did not wish them to know my current embarrassment. They asked about my family and expressed sincere feelings regarding the death of my Father, your Brother, in the summer of this year and my Mothers passing away almost ten years ago now. I would not permit this to dampen the degree of amusement and interest that these gentlemen seemed to derive from hearing of my every twist and turn and indeed if there were ever two people capable of raising the spirits then I soon discovered it to be Mr Richard Fenton and his son John.

I revealed that my attention was now drawn to that most mysterious of destinations, the magnet for every insatiable tourist, Stonehenge. This news could not have pleased the two gentlemen more as this was the very purpose in spending the night here at the Deptford Inn so that they might make that identical excursion in the morning. It was made very clear that no protest on my part was going to be sufficient to dissuade them from extending an invitation for me to join them in this venture. Mr Richard Fenton informed me that I would be required to suspend my pedestrianism for the day as they were to place themselves entirely in the hands of "the pilot of the plains" their good friend and fellow antiquary, Mr William Cunnington. This learned gentleman would be arriving shortly after breakfast in his carriage and the order of events thereon would be undertaken solely under his direction. I had no choice but to agree to this arrangement, so forcibly was it proposed and it would also give my ankle a further degree of rest after today's exertions.

Mr John Fenton had by now excused himself to ensure that the two identical ladies with whom they had shared a carriage earlier this evening were not wanting for some company after their dinner. His Father suggested that a singular offspring of that family would have been sufficient in attracting his attention but to multiply this vision by two would only serve to hasten the process and double his efforts. As the night was clear and cold we were glad to draw our chairs up to the fire and I now asked Mr Fenton after his family. He informed me that he resided in Fishguard, a town in the county of Pembrokeshire with his dear wife Eliza and their three sons of which John is the eldest. Mr Fenton explained that it was through the investigation of the history of his native county of Pembrokeshire that he had the good fortune to become acquainted with Sir Richard Colt Hoare of Stourhead in Wiltshire. The two gentlemen had spent many pleasurable summer excursions together unravelling the mysteries that lay within the barrows and cromlechs of that place and had become firm friends. Sir Richard Colt Hoare's gaze was now drawn to the horizons of his own county of Wiltshire and in combination with the gentleman that I shall have the good fortune to meet tomorrow, Mr William Cunnington, a great deal of antiquarian investigation has already been undertaken here. The Baronet, for that is indeed the master of Stourhead's correct title, is now embarking on the most ambitious of projects, a great work entitled "The Ancient History of Wiltshire". In stentorian tones Mr Fenton gave full vent in support of this grand undertaking, raising his glass in a most theatrical and humorous manner: "We shall speak from facts not theory and every barrow that raises its dome above the green sward and has not already been violated by the curious or the tomb robber, shall be cracked open like a hot egg and its contents spooned out, poured over and their meaning digested. It shall be nothing short of an antiquarian feast". Mr Fenton then smiled at his own outburst but assured me it would be a pioneering work with new maps and surveys on a scale never before attempted and every article uncovered is to be illustrated in full by an expert employed to the task. I did not like to presume that one day I should dearly like to meet the Baronet and contented myself that tomorrow would bring its own opportunities with the elucidation of a subject in which Mr John Fenton and I were to be initiates.

Mr John Fenton then returned from his attendance to the travelling twins to stir the fire vigorously as if to relieve his frustrations. He then turned his attention to me and spoke in a very earnest fashion. " Henry, there go two of the handsomest young women that I have ever had the good fortune to encounter, who are away to the City of Bath in the morning and where are we going I ask? Answer; to visit a jumble of rocks in a barren wasteland. What say you to this?" I had not before met with this kind of talk and I took the younger Mr Fenton's stance very seriously and indeed

began to defend Stonehenge confirming my own
enthusiasm for the visit. Mr Richard Fenton smiled
and said that I should have to become accustomed to
his sons ways for "He often speaks to witness the
effects of his words on others. It is called raillery and
it is an art in which he is already a master. I can
assure you Sir that he is as keen on this long awaited
visit as yourself but wishes to suggest to you, as you
are a young man with the same susceptible warm
blood in your veins as he, that the City of Bath is now
a worthy diversion and is soon to be doubly bolstered
in its attractions although neither redeeming feature
on this occasion are of an antiquarian or geological
nature."

"Exactly Father" Confirmed the other. The two Mr
Fentons' made no indication that they were about to
retire for the evening as they were content to refill
their glasses and enjoy the fire. I expressed my
pleasure and good fortune in making their
acquaintance and bid them both a good night,
conscious also of my duties with the pen. My wrist is
now aching but it is a labour in which I feel a growing
pleasure and satisfaction for without it my stumblings

here in South Wiltshire would have no purpose. I
thank you for your patience my Dear Uncle and wish
you a good night also.

Your persistent Nephew
HENRY CHALK

Tuesday 13th October 1807

M Y DEAR UNCLE,

Immediately upon meeting our guide for the day, Mr William Cunnington, I felt at ease in his company for he is a kindly man whose every effort is given over to ensuring to the needs and comfort of others. Some gentlemen are attentive only when listening to the tone of their own voice and can smother any conversation, our host and pilot could not be more at odds with this type as he is very thoughtful and considers deeply the words of others before responding. You may be certain, my Dear Uncle, that I am much taken with Mr Cunnington after but one day in his company and I have a great deal of sympathy also as he suffers from the most severe headaches that are both sudden in their onset and are greatly debilitating.

Once we had settled our business with the Landlord of the Deptford Inn, I joined our host in combination with the two Mr Fentons' and our

carriage was soon to begin its long and slow ascent to
Yarnbury Castle. On reaching this great plateau that
marks the beginning proper of Salisbury Plain we
found a vast earthen camp that is circular with deep
ditches and great grass banks and there exists a large
central expanse within the entrenchments. Mr
Cunnington informed us, whilst we were still within
his carriage, that a great sheep fair is held each year
at this place on October 5th and indeed there are
indications on the ground where sheep pens and
compounds have lately been established and then
abandoned. Today we had for company an icy wind
that travelled without interruption from the north east
across the open plain and only at the base of the
deepest ditch was there any respite. Witnessing my
discomfort and seeing that I had not sufficient
clothing for this exposure Mr Cunnington kindly
offered me a thick coat from under the seating within
the coach. Mr John Fenton was similarly attired but
believed his coat had a rank odour although he only
expressed this view in hushed tones to myself. I
reasoned that it was the strong animal residue from
the recent sheep fair that filled our nostrils and the

overcoats were not to be blamed and I assured my travelling companion of this fact. We now began a circuit of the place and it was soon apparent that it is a position that has been chosen with care for there is a good aspect in all directions. On the neighbouring ridge, and across the valley lay Grovelly wood and my thoughts again turned to Peter Winter and Tam and for the moment I envied their life amongst the shelter of the woodland for at the centre of their world was always a warming fire. Beyond the ridge I could again see the top of the tower that I had observed with Tam as we travelled by cart to the New Inn and it has occurred to me that it is an object that I had first sighted even before my arrival in Salisbury. From the roof of the London coach I had witnessed the distant spire yet beyond that existed a duplicate interruption to the horizon to which at the time I had paid little regard as I believed that my vision had been impaired by the terrific jolting that I had received. I fully intended to establish what structure it was that could possibly compete with Salisbury Cathedral yet as we walked along the crest of the outer battlements any words uttered were soon discarded by the wind. My thoughts turned to a dark and turbulent history that has determined such an undertaking here and also on the slopes across the valley on the Grovelly ridge. To inhabit such places is to spurn the shelter of the valleys and a great fear has driven these ancient peoples to draw up the earth and chalk around them on such a grand scale. It is an enterprise requiring an enormous degree of labour that in the world today I can only compare to the creation of our new canals.

At the event of our completion of the circuit I quite forgot to resolve the puzzle of the mysterious tower as my thoughts were trained on the sanctuary of Mr Cunnington's carriage. Once inside our host clapped his hands together and expressed his pleasure at the invigorating effects of the clean and dry air of this place. Mr Richard Fenton, who is himself no stranger to Salisbury Plain, concurred wholeheartedly and produced a small flask from his pocket which he then passed amongst us. I had not before tasted strong liquor and it caused a sudden coughing and spluttering as it passed my throat which provided much merriment and laughter within the carriage. Once the fiery effects of the liquid had calmed

sufficiently, I conceded that there was an eventual
pleasant taste to the experience. Mr John Fenton was
all for administering another dose to make me repeat
the spectacle but Mr Cunnington kindly advised
against this and then knocked on the carriage roof
with the handle of his cane as a signal to the
coachman to continue with our excursion.

As we made our way to the next point of
antiquarian interest, I must have looked thoughtful in
my silence as Mr Cunnington, who occupied the seat
opposite to myself then asked for my view of Yarnbury
Castle. It was a request that caught me off my guard
and after consideration I felt that as I was a stranger to
this county and also to the study of the ancient
peoples of this land I believed that I was therefore
unqualified to offer an opinion and I informed our
guide as such. As I had now become accustomed, Mr
Cunnington paused before responding. "Then I would
judge that you are surprised and not a little
disappointed that your guide cannot elucidate the
matter of who, why and when regarding Yarnbury
Castle, am I not correct?" I felt myself redden and it
was as if the gentleman sat before me could read my

very thoughts and I began to fluster. Mr Cunnington held up his hand to prevent any apology on my part and then continued; "Beware of any man who talks with absolute certainty on any subject as there will always be more to learn. I have listened to the great and the learned who from their study of ancient manuscripts and of the classics are wholly convinced of their correctness. I put it to you Sir that Mr Henry Chalk is equally as capable as Mr William Cunnington or indeed as any rational man, in resolving the who, why and when conundrum. I would direct this also to Mr John Fenton. The answer lies out there in the soil amongst the banks and the ditches and with the broken pottery and the burials and not yet on the shelves of the greatest libraries. I am a wool merchant who is neglecting his business to play my small part in unravelling these mysteries, I fear though that I shall not live to see the day when there exists a clarity and understanding of the lives and struggles of our great ancestors. Mr John Fenton and yourself however are fortunate to have that future in store and to live in an era where I sense there are great opportunities ahead." Mr Cunnington then paused to look at both aspiring antiquarians in turn to emphasize this statement, " I would not bring you both to Yarnbury Castle and then desert you without offering some scrap of an explanation, for it is indeed little more. There are some that would place it firmly with the Saxons and the Danes but it is my own view that it was a place of occupation and security of the British aboriginals before even the arrival of our Roman masters. There, I have said enough."

The rain now thrashed at the outside of our coach and we all expressed our pity for the poor driver and Mr Fenton again circulated his flask to which I politely declined. I then produced my pocketful of "panshards" that I had collected before departing from Grovelly and Mr Cunnington looked on with curiosity "Well you have begun already, that was swift action indeed." He studied the pieces, identifying some fine Roman work which has a bright red colouring and is exceedingly well made whilst the remainder is dull and crude in appearance. The coinage He described as that used by the Ancient Britons but offered caution as to whether there was at that time a general circulation of currency amongst

the population. Mr Richard Fenton then looked
sternly upon his son John and questioned his
contribution to this research and when the young man
offered a blank expression in return his father
proclaimed loudly that he had brought shame on the
family name and he should go forth on his hands and
knees and retrieve some of the same without delay. I
confess I find it difficult not to show my amusement
when in Mr Fenton's company as so often he is intent
on mockery and theatrics and would not be ill suited
to the stage.

Our carriage halted at a crossroads where Mr
Cunnington lamented that he had hoped to escort us
to the most extraordinary array of ancient burial
mounds which were so perfectly arranged that you
can draw a straight line through their centres once
their positions are laid out in a plan. As the rain fell
unabated our guide did not wish to subject us to a
soaking before we reached our primary goal and he
prayed that we should at least have an opportunity to
inspect Stonehenge in some degree of comfort.
Through the rain distorted glass of the carriage
window I could observe one enormous mound of a

considerable length to which Mr Cunnington referred,
not without good reason, as a "long barrow". These,
He stated, were once supposed to be battle barrows
and they were necessarily large due to the heavy
mortality of the combat, with the slain being buried at
the site of the conflict. Our guide was now at odds
with this view but confessed ignorance as to the
reason for the great scale of these tombs although he
could report that no metal goods had been unearthed
in their investigation thus far from which we may
draw our own conclusions. The remainder in this
curious line were "bowl barrows", "bell barrows",
"pond barrows" and "druid barrows" and as Mr
Cunnington signalled to the coachman to proceed he
promised the present company a return excursion as
it was a sight worthy of a detailed inspection. Mr
Fenton, who had before visited the prehistoric
cemetery, then stated that if you were a barrow
purchaser planning in advance of your demise you
could do no better than view the array on offer at this
location as the variety was unsurpassed in his
estimation with a suitable tomb for every need and
occasion. He then added with sincerity that a great

many of the barrows in the vicinity of Stonehenge and indeed across the breadth of Salisbury Plain had undergone a thorough examination by our guide and it was a plague of the most severe case of modesty that prevented that same gentleman from giving a detailed account of their nature and content. Mr Fenton also recommended a future visit to view the produce of these investigations at the home of Mr Cunnington in Heytesbury where they are on display in an annexe called the "Moss House" and have caused great curiosity and fascination to those who have already signed the visitor book. The proprietor of that place acknowledged that nothing would please him more and he then made the curious suggestion that we should raise the window shutters and travel in darkness to our next destination.

Mr Cunnington's carriage finally came to a standstill and there was a pause before our guide broke the silence; "Gentlemen, welcome to Stonehenge". The weather had been kind for as the driver opened the door we were greeted by the brilliance of the sun for the showers had temporarily abated yet the wind had not lost its icy thrust and we drew our coats tightly around

us in preparation. From the dark confinement of the
carriage we were forced now to shield our eyes as we
climbed down onto the green sward and then cowered
before these giant stones until we became accustomed
to this exposure. It is one matter to view illustrations of
Stonehenge in books but that reduction in scale gives
no impression of the true experience of confronting this
ancient structure. Mr Fenton threw up his arms and
called out above the wind "How Grand!, How
Wonderful!, How Incomprehensible!" A statement I
believe that voiced all our thoughts. Mr Cunnington
then summoned us together to explain his hidden
purpose for arriving in darkness. "To witness
Stonehenge from afar is not the correct approach as it is
dwarfed by its open surrounds and this insignificance
then disappoints. To behold it as we have today, and so
it has been proven to me on many an occasion, is the
only method. It is an inconvenience for which I
apologise, but I sincerely hope that you are in
agreement that it is an exercise that is worthwhile in its
effect". Our party was unanimous in support of this
action and we then commended our guide on his good
reason and judgement.

As with all the illustrations of this place that I have viewed in the British Museum Library there is always a flock of sheep and attendant shepherd in view as if by some ancient agreement and we were not to be disappointed today. In no time this wind weathered and toothless figure had presumed to avail himself on our party and furnish us with all the details as he perceived them and how he had felt the ground shake with the falling of "Thic gurt stone" some eight years ago which narrowly missed him but took one of his Master's flock. Mr Cunnington took out his purse and pressed a small coin onto the watcher over the stones, I believe on the understanding that the fellow should return to his drifting flock and then leave the narration of this place to the guide appointed to the task. The shepherd departed after recording his success with a gesture to the north east "Looks sauf 'twur gwain to rain snaw" and cast his eye about to register some reaction to this prophecy. I was all for practising my local tongue but Mr Cunnington gently dissuaded me least I should encourage the man and he returned to impart more of his wisdom. Our guide apologised for demanding that our attention for a moment should be drawn to the two differing rocks on display. The larger inner pairings of stones with their capping lintels are named "Trilithons" and are constructed of a rock local to Salisbury Plain termed "Sarcen", which is a form of surface sandstone and I am informed that it is plentiful in its natural state in the Marlborough area. The outer circle is of the same material and before the ravishes of time would have formed a perfect ring, capped with lintels. The second type of rock, which makes up an inner ring of smaller uprights and also a horseshoe shape, or a broken oval, are a variety of granite and hornstone and perhaps originate from some part of Devonshire or Cornwall. Mr Cunnington believed that the smaller stones were a later addition to the design and to experience the vision of the unknown architect of Stonehenge we must imagine only the complete "Sarcen" structure and banish the later imports from our thoughts. We then entering the circle and our group dispersed to wander and weave between the ruin while the sun retreated behind a cloud that was darker than the very stone of this place. I sheltered for a brief interval, with my back against one of the pair of uprights that formed a colossal "Trilithon" and I then closed my eyes to listen to the song of the wind as it passed between the stones. Was it the sound of the wind or the sound of the stone for there could not be one without the other? With my palms flat on the rock behind me I sensed that my fingertips had traced slight depressions in the surface and I turned to inspect what may be designs or rough carvings although I could not easily make out their form. I left the sanctuary of the "Trilithon" and wondered at the hollows created in the fallen lintels to enable their secure attachment when resting on the uprights, as there is a nodule that has been formed there to fit into these depressions. It brings to my mind the construction of heavy timber frames that I have observed in the repairs to the roof of the brewery in Southall for it is a similar form of jointing. On one of the smaller uprights I detected where a portion had been struck, perhaps by some tourist's hammer, and a remnant lay on the grass which I inspected and found it quite speckled in colour. When my tour is finally over my pockets shall be fairly overcrowded with items of antiquarian and geological interest.

I cannot believe that I have made such a long account of the day's activities and I fear that there is still a little more to report. It is not an excursion that is made perhaps more than once in a lifetime by the majority and yet I feel certain that one day I shall return for there is so much more to observe. This evening I have forfeited my evening meal as my resources do not permit me to join the two Mr Fentons, here at the George Inn in Amesbury. I have made my excuses that I have an ailing stomach when in truth it is crying out to be fed. Mr Cunnington has suffered a severe headache and has returned at once to his home in Heytesbury and I have commented already on these bouts which so often afflict this poor gentleman.

I return once more, My Dear Uncle, to the events of the day and our small group gathered at the "Hele Stone", which is set on the periphery of Stonehenge. There is a significance of the alignment of this irregular stone as on the morning of the longest day of the year the sun will rise from above this stone and is witnessed by those situated within the main circle of Stonehenge. There is much talk of "Druids" and their

ceremonies of which I know not what to make and
certainly Mr William Stukeley is an advocate of this
practice. This same alignment is also represented by
a broad course that runs between two parallel banks
and I could detect this route as it passed across the
closely cropped grassland. Our guide informed us
that this was the "Avenue" and it was first recognised
by the same Mr Stukeley and it forms the main
approach to Stonehenge in the darkness of the
midsummer   morning   before   the   ceremony
commences. I sensed that our visit was concluding
and I requested that I should be permitted to follow
the "Avenue" for a short distance along its descent
from the stone circle. Had I realised that Mr
Cunnington was ailing even at this stage I would not
have wished to protract the visit, but as there was
already rain in the air I promised to be as swift as my
weak ankle would permit. As the party returned to the
shelter of the carriage I departed in the opposite
direction anbd I very soon found myself at the base of
the shallow valley. With the rain beating down on me
I turned to find Stonehenge now completely obscured
by the slope with only the parallel banks of the

"Avenue" to guide me back to my destination. As the wind urged at my back, slowly the tops of the stones and their lintels came into my view until the whole of the form dominated the horizon in perfect orientation and it was as if the structure was once again complete. This was surely the correct and only approach to Stonehenge and yet if this way were made in darkness on midsummer morning the effect would be lost. The sun rises in the east and sets in the west and I wonder that we are facing the wrong direction and at the wrong time of day for when you approach along the "Avenue" with all its dramatic effect, this should be undertaken in daylight and observers would look not back to the east but directly ahead to the west. There must be some equidistance relating to the sunrise and sunset between the longest and shortest days in the calendar year and perhaps the end of the shortest day is the event that should be witnessed by looking to the west through the correct apertures of this giant stone arrangement. From this day grows the slow lengthening of the day light hour which must surely be a cause for celebration with the prospect of a new year and the seasons of growth and fertility ahead and

we can emerge from our time of darkness. I rushed
back to the carriage as quick as I was able to propose
this fanciful notion to Mr Cunnington but I found him
cradling his head in his hands and I was full of
apology at delaying our departure and protracting our
guide's agonies and torment. There is so much more
that I would like to ask of this gentleman concerning
Stonehenge and other matters and I dearly hope that
one day we shall meet again.

One cannot visit this place without formulating
some notion as to its purpose and it is then customary
to write at length about it to convince the world of
your own wisdom and the shortsightedness of others.
There, I have now accomplished that tradition and I
am afraid, my Dear Uncle, that you have been the
unfortunate recipient.

I have received a visitor to my room. Mr John
Fenton appeared, as I was in the process of cleaning
my own boots, an act to which I was surprised that he
made no reference and instead he proceeded to ask
after my health. He then produced a bottle of port
wine and two glasses claiming it a remedy for my
ailment, and he filled these glasses until they could

take no more and then pressed one upon me,
encouraging me to drink it as he was certain that it
would do me some good. He then bemoaned the fact
that Mr Cunnington had returned home and his
Father was attending to his journal. His eyes fell on
my own account of the day as I had not yet committed
the pages to an envelope and before I could prevent it,
or make my protest, he gathered up the sheets of
paper from the table and held them aloft; "Henry, you
have written this much? We have been in each other's
company throughout this day and made the same
visits yet your account has filled all this. With what, I
ask you?" He then began to leaf through the papers
and then kept the pile from my grasp as I tried to
retrieve them. "I do not wish to pry Sir," The younger
Mr Fenton assured me "But it is an overwhelming
curiosity for I could not fill one side of a piece of
paper with my recollections of the events of the day".
His eyes fell on one passage and I feared that I had
made some reference to this gentleman that would
offend and embarrass. "The "mysterious tower" to
which you refer, I can assist you with that particular
detail. It is the tower belonging to Mr William

Beckford's great folly; Fonthill Abbey. You have not heard of this most wealthy of gentlemen?" When I informed Mr John Fenton that I only knew of him that he prevented the local huntsmen from gaining access to his grounds and that it was a sanctuary for foxes, he nodded and confirmed that this was indeed a view acknowledged by all who were aware of Mr Beckford and his inclinations. He then thought for a moment and continued; " Mr Henry Chalk, I wager you the sum of five guineas that you cannot ascend Mr Beckford's tower, we are soon to return to Stourhead and if you put up at the Stourhead Inn we can there settle the issue. What say you to this?" Wishing only for the return of my papers and this access was to be denied save only by the shaking of this young gentleman's hand, I did so, and the correspondence was returned. My glass was refilled and Mr John Fenton then proceeded to tell me that life can become dull without a wager here and a wager there and he rubbed his hands together as if life had of a sudden become more exciting now that this wager was set and hanging in the air. Having enlivened his evening Mr John Fenton then departed with his bottle and I

confess my Dear Uncle that my hand is now at odds
with my head after the intoxication of the port wine
and I bid you goodnight.

HENRY C

Thursday 15th October 1807

MY DEAR UNCLE,

I write now in a state of absolute confusion and fatigue and I am resigned to giving over the day here at the Stourhead Inn to commit to paper the details as best as I am able in the order that they occurred for it seems an age ago since the evening of my wager with the younger Mr Fenton. I have slept for two hours since my arrival here earlier this morning though I feel sure that I will be required to rest again before this day is through.

I left the George Inn at Amesbury before daybreak on Wednesday morning unable to take breakfast due to the effects of the port wine which I have vowed never to touch again in this lifetime and my head still throbs at its very mention. Unsettled by that evil tincture and with my thoughts spinning I felt a heavy cloud of uncertainty hanging over me with the prospect of my fulfilment of the wager and I spent the night in a cold clam sweat. After settling with the

Landlord and paying the price of the postage for my correspondence I calculated that I had sufficient for one further nights lodging only. As you will recall my Dear Uncle I have already forfeited one evening meal although on the morning of my departure from Amesbury, food could not have been further from my thoughts.

Having seen so little of this county I found myself following in reverse the course of Monday's excursion and I passed by Stonehenge in the early morning gloom. I had forgotten the feelings of excitement from yesterdays visit for these shadowy stones now threatened my nerves and appeared as a mustering of darkly cloaked figures intent on conspiracy and I was glad to find that I had passed from their view.

There was some early traffic on the road and I met a flying eastbound stage at the burial cemetery crossroads. I am still in possession of my thumbstick to which I have become greatly attached although I have found it at times in my right hand so I gauge that it has become less of a necessary support for my left ankle and more a comfort and a reminder also of Peter Winter.

The small village of Winterbourne Stoke was coming to life yet I believe no one person noticed as this sallow figure slowly arrived and departed. The climb to Yarnbury Castle seemed to be without end and as I viewed its lumpy shape on the horizon I appeared not to be making any distance towards it and so I flopped down under a roadside apple tree. The bulk of the fruit from the tree lay about the grass but I could not bring myself to taste it although I picked up a handful of the small rosy red apples to keep for my journey. I sipped at water from a bottle which was my salvation and I thank you again My Dear Uncle for the help and guidance that your small publication has assisted this simple and foolish traveller for without water I believe that I would die. In a vacant mood I read for a while from my book "A Sentimental Journey" by Lawrence Sterne which has kept me in quiet amusement although I do not really know why.

In time I picked myself up and filled my head with all manner of nonsense to distract myself from the act of walking until I eventually drew level with Yarnbury Castle. I could now look across to the object of my

wager, the very top of the tower of Fonthill Abbey and
how my empty stomach sank more and I confess that I
retched again at this sight although my stomach could
not have been more vacant. After descending to the
village of Wylye I stopped at the river and watched
the bright green weed snaking in the flow and then
rinsed my face in its clear cold waters. I observed as a
distant figure worked in the regular ditches and grass
causeways that lay across the valley floor and I had
seen before, when I had passed through this place on
my way to the Deptford Inn, the stone blocks and
wooden hatches that must combine to control the
flooding of this land. The corn mill nearby was all
noise and motion with gushing water and grinding
gears within that shook the very ground under my
feet. Carts were hauling to and fro and it was all
together too busy and loud for my delicate condition
but this is a fine river that supports life and industry
here and I imagine in many other places along its
entire course.

My spirits rose as the morning grew older and I did
not now care whether my wager was won or lost for I
was alive. The day was clear with small puffs of white

cloud drifting slowly across a pale blue sky and it was as if summer had returned but the rustling of the leaves gave a clue to the advancement of the seasons and no warm trickery of the sun can halt this decay into autumn. My carefree notions took a sharp turn with my first full view of Fonthill Abbey. This colossal form is promoted to the full by its placement on a high ridge and its surrounds are a brooding forest of dark green and it appears a most forbidding place. When I reached Fonthill Bishop I was confronted with the great stone gateway to the estate that I believe spans the public road. Having passed only humble dwellings with mouldy thatch and crumbling walls this structure is bold and shouts aloud of wealth and prosperity. I passed as silently as I could beneath this giant arch thinking that at any time a great booming voice would question my purpose here but I met with no one. The land here has changed of a sudden from the gently rolling bulk of Salisbury Plain with which I am now more familiar to a lush parkland of majestic trees, strange shrubs and a long glistening lake. I found great curiosity in an activity taking place not far from the road which was all dust and

destruction and at first I thought it a stone quarry
from the amount of carts loaded with blocks of stone
departing from the site. On taking a closer look I
could see the foundations of a former building that
once occupied this position and a portion had
escaped intact from which I could gauge the design
and immense scale of the original. I enquired whether
a great fire had caused this extraordinary destruction
but I was informed by a labourer that this was not the
case and that it was simply "Master's orders, tis
shame but there tis".

I continued to a crossroads where there is a busy
Inn with many post chaises and coaches lingering
outside and I asked for directions to Fonthill Abbey
of an old hunched maid who was transporting a great
pile of dried branches on her back. She gestured that
I should continue straight across and she hurried on
her way shaking her old wrinkled nut brown head and
taking her own counsel on the matter. In a short while
I was following a road through woodland and I
stopped some distance short of the gatehouse and lay
on a grassy bank to observe the comings and goings.
There is every sign that uninvited guests and

intruders are not welcome here as the stone block wall of twelve feet or more is fortified with iron spikes. I was passed by a succession of tourists who pulled up at the entrance in their chaises and were then turned away by the gatekeeper and I pondered how my own challenge could be fulfilled. I began a sketch of the scene with the Abbey looming up high above the wood, its carcass and great neck clad in a blur of scaffolding as if some great arachnid had ensnared the beast. The sketch is incomplete but I forward it to you My Dear Uncle as I have committed myself to send you all that is engendered by my foolish travails. I was disturbed from my labour with the pencil by a short elderly gentleman who halted his single horse carriage alongside my position and then disembarked. I know not how to place these words politely as his purpose was to relieve himself of some liquid burden and he had begun this operation before noticing my presence. This gentleman did not appear overly concerned at my close proximity and even raised his hat and after bidding me a good afternoon he requested that he might observe my effort with the pencil. After completing his original task he took my sketchbook and studied the drawing thoughtfully but I soon realised that it was the subject that had prompted his reverie and not my ability as an artist. "I am late" the Gentleman reflected before handing back my work without comment. I enquired as to what hour he should have been in attendance as I sensed that he was destined for the Abbey itself and here perhaps lay my opportunity. His reply could not have surprised me more; "Young Sir, it is not the o'clock that is the problem, it is the calendar month" and with that statement he climbed aboard his chaise. I hurriedly introduced myself and stated the terms of my foolish quest to which he responded with great charity; "All I know sir is that you are a young artist and it is a singular breed that may be more welcome than most into the lair of the Caliph of Fonthill. Permit me to introduce myself, I am Mr James Wyatt the architect of that great folly on the hill". He then indicated that I should show some haste if my intention was to join him in his chaise and I quickly gathered up my belongings and bundled myself aboard. Sitting next to this gentleman I could now sense a strong fruity odour and he looked very weary with dark shadows around his eyes and I believe Sir that he was "in his cups". Our carriage halted before the entrance and from the expression of the gatekeeper he was obviously familiar with the Gentleman by my side for he did not hesitate in opening the gate and he touched his hat as we passed by and called out; "Mr Wyatt Zur" and as an afterthought he added "N' the young Gent'man Zur?" but Mr Wyatt was not for pausing to discuss the matter of my identity with the gatekeeper and he ushered the horse to trot away at speed. The way was steep and the straps tightened on the flanks of the horse as it laboured under the encouragement given by the driver with his whip. There were many twists and turns with dense green foliage on our right and between the trees on our left I caught sight of a sheet of water which gave me some surprise as I did not expect to find a lake at this height and at some distance from the valley bottom. I took this opportunity to ask the architect of Fonthill Abbey about the destruction of the large house near the giant stone archway and he shook his head in some dismay before answering; " Ahh Splendens, a very grand building, indeed a perfectly adequate building, that stood for barely fifty years since its rebuilding after a fire in 1755. In truth for all the past wealth of this accursed family, and it has been Sir on an extraordinary scale, quite extraordinary, dear old Splendens has now fallen with the sugar market as Mr Beckford has not the money or materials for his project and so his Father's house has now paid that price. Mr Beckford is not one who is prone to remorse or regret and cares not a brass farthing for what I or anybody else thinks. I have made my protest Sir, but to no avail" The architect then explained how at first cement had been utilised in combination with timber throughout the new property but this method was deemed inferior and all was now being removed and the reclaimed stone from the earlier house was being used in its stead.

At length we reached level ground and it is on this open and elevated plane that Mr William Beckford's giant new curiosity is at present undergoing its construction and I drew a gasp at the enormity of the sight before me. "Now Sir" said Mr Wyatt as we drew to a halt, "my business takes me to the rear of the building. I suggest you take the main doors on the western side and there you can make an entrance. Good day young Sir and pray be on your guard." I had barely time to climb down and thank the Gentleman before he had cracked his whip and trotted on.

My Dear Uncle I am now very tired and I must put down my pen and seek sustenance and also rest a while. I can heartily recommend the Stourhead Inn as the service is excellent and the beds are soft, clean and dry.

My Dear Uncle how my life has changed and I wish I could race to describe that moment and share it with you but my story must unfold as it occurred for you to make any sense of it. I have yet to make my approach to Fonthill Abbey and I must for the time being dispel all other thoughts and place myself on those closely cropped lawns and savour the resinous odours from the strange trees and plants that abound in Mr Beckford's estate. At first I felt that the distance between myself and this immense structure was not in any way being reduced and that I was simply lifting my feet up and down to no effect. I viewed the industry amongst the scaffolding, the endless lengths

of rope hauling up stone and timber, with tiny
creatures massing in groups that I knew to be
labourers and like cannon blasts from a great distant
galleon there were puffs of dust and scatterings of
fallen debris raining down. I reasoned that these
small explosions were caused by the crumbling and
spillage of the cement material as it was being
removed to be then replaced with block stone. In
accordance with Mr Wyatt's instructions I made a
circuit to the western side and was straining my neck
to view its every detail but I was disadvantaged by the
sheer size of this building and as I drew ever closer I
found I could look up no more. Finally I climbed the
steps before the Western Entrance and I could only
wonder at the dimension of the pair of doors that
towered above me and laughed out loud as I recalled
the words of the Architect of this place; "There you
can make an entrance". I rapped on the solid studded
wood as if tapping on a great oak tree, such was the
impression made by my poor knuckles. I tried again
using all my force with the end of my walking stick
yet as with knocking on any door, one must wait for an
answer although I was in full doubt that any inside

could hear my efforts. To my great surprise I could hear faint steps from within the building and I straightened my appearance and stood, and stood, and stood my Dear Uncle as the footsteps grew in volume and with this waiting my heart beat ever faster. Surely the ogre of Fonthill would not answer his own front door. At last there was a huge echoing clunk as a latch or a bolt was drawn and these great arched doors silently drifted apart. The aperture grew wider and I looked upwards at the effect of this opening yet there seemed no human agency involved in this operation. Indeed I should have looked down as there stood between these giant slabs of wood a minute gentleman dressed in an embroidered gold costume. At this extraordinary vision and gross conflict of scale I could not utter a single syllable while this tiny servant screwed up his face and even picked at his nose as he observed me. It was then as if a thought had occurred to him for he looked puzzled and after this odd succession of facial contortions he finally spoke; "You have come from London? Is Franchi with you?" His voice had a rasp to it and I judged that he was an English speaking foreigner. At last I found my voice and answered truthfully that I had indeed embarked from London and I was alone. The small man then stood aside for me to enter to which I obliged and with barely a touch of one finger he reunited these giant doors and seemed to take no small amount of pleasure from his control of their smooth and silent motion. The refastening of the latch echoed around a cavernous hall and I looked about the place in wonder; at the floor, the walls and the vaulted roof. The golden servant grunted an instruction for me to follow and I puzzled at my reception here and that my appearance was in some way expected and yet this could not be possible and I knew no person by the name of Franchi. The boots of the servant made a great clicking as he marched ahead of me and at first I thought there was a curious odour to this place yet I realised that it emanated from this little man as I trailed silently in his wake. Standing in a recess on the side wall was a statue of a man frozen in a position of animated speech and on the floor beneath this figure was a diminutive table and chair with paper, ink and pen at the ready. I gauged by the size of the furniture that the little servant had been at this position when he responded to my tappings on the great door for no other soul would have heard. We changed levels to a vast chamber and the little gentleman raised a hand as an indication that I should wait as he then disappeared behind a drapery of deep crimson that extended up beyond the height of most town houses. I realised that I was standing in an octagon and as there were a corresponding eight sides to the great tower then I must be directly at its base. I moved to the centre of this space and span slowly around. My Dear uncle it is as if the ink well of my own thoughts and imagination has run dry for I know not where to begin a description of this place. All is awe and I looked in vain for some familiar object to reassure and on which to rest my gaze but found none. Everywhere is light and darkness and I am bathed in yellow and purple sunshine as the coloured glass of these vast windows is projected across the stone floor and this effect floats across the enormous purple and crimson draperies that adorn these walls. Heavy black furniture forms a further contrast and indeed on studying these pieces I find that they are studded with a white ivory and so it seems that every detail here is attended to. I am of the conviction that these effects are designed to perplex the viewer and transport him from the known world to a place of fantasy. It is a building constructed for a tribe of giants and I could not believe that any normal being could make this his abode without soon descending into madness. I heard brisk footsteps approach and the creator of this vision appeared and then stopped abruptly in the doorway to observe me and even from across this great open chamber I was taken aback by his unblinking stare. For the second time in only a short period my words would not form. I know not for how long we stood in silence before Mr William Beckford spoke out with his high voice echoing around the place like that of a choir boy in a cathedral. "So you have not travelled to Ireland?". I was much taken aback by this question and also further convinced that my presence here was confused with the expected arrival of another and I simply shook my head in response. Sympathetic to my obvious discomfort, although not suspecting its cause, in a sudden movement the owner of this place was now standing before me and stopped just short of holding onto my arm. He studied me closely; "You seem . . . more . . . " His observation remained unvoiced and his mood then relaxed "Dwarfish courtesy has not extended to offering you refreshment after your journey? No? no, of course he has not, it was never his strongest suit and you must I fear excuse him as he is excitable for today he presides at the head of the election dinner in my stead. It is a small matter of my return to parliament and it is a tiresome and costly business and a bacchanalian orgy of excess, all of which I cannot abide. The poor fellow has set up his table and chair at the feet of Alderman Beckford in the vain hope of drawing inspiration for his election address but he will be too drunk to read his own illiterate scrawl so it matters little." Mr Beckford then clapped his hands together in a quick volley not as a summons to his domestic but out of irrepressible excitement which seemed to be brought about by my presence which puzzled and worried me in equal proportions. When the servant did appear, He was flicked away as an irritation although the domestic bravely persisted and informed his Master that Mr Wyatt the architect had arrived. The messenger retreated and in the purple and yellow light Mr Beckford slowly encircled me "Yes you are a deal older and more worldly than I recall from that night at the Circus Royal. In my imagination I have you as a child genius of the tightrope yet now I see that it is all theatrical effect . . . I have ropes aplenty here . . . " He let out a long sigh and informed me that he had business with his architect that could not be delayed and he insisted that I should eat and rest. I stammered that I should dearly like to ascend the tower, a request that clearly irritated my misguided host. "The tower, the tower, is that all that is of interest to the entire world?" Then of a sudden he caught me by the hand and pulled me in his wake. "Come and see the wretched tower," His voice ringing instructions to summon the assistant to the clerk of works and he then cast me adrift and flew to his outstanding appointment with Mr Wyatt.

My appointed escort duly arrived carrying a lantern and he was a large nervous gentleman who spoke little. We began the ascent of a seemingly incessant spiral of stone steps and the lantern was immediately warranted for without it we would be in complete darkness as there was not a single aperture. As shadows flickered and I followed the bulky form of my guide, I lost my count of how many times around we went until daylight was obtained once more and we emerged into a gallery. From this position I could overlook the axis of the entire building where I had awaited the arrival of Mr Beckford and I tried not to consider how I was going to exit this place without causing embarrassment and anger for I had already sensed a flash of his temper. The way ahead was a jumble of steps and ladders into unfinished rooms heaped with building debris and with glimpses through windows I had small previews of the eventual vista from the summit. We could hear the calling and the chattering of the workforce from the scaffolding beyond the walls as we climbed a final succession of ladders to the apex of this giant construction. My guide was breathing noisily and we could access no further than this eight-sided room and each wall had its corresponding open and unglazed window. I immediately went from one opening to next, around and around and at first my eyes were streaming with the effects of the air and wind at this altitude and I could see little more than a division between blue and green. As my vision cleared I requested of my guide the names and whereabouts of distant features and I realised that the poor gentleman was reluctant to leave the centre of the room and was in some discomfort; "Truth be told sur, I fears the heights and I reckons thas why he do send me to this task", to which I apologised and was then very conscious of not protracting his discomfort and I could now understand his reticence throughout my indulgent excursion. I wish, My Dear Uncle that you could be with me at the very top of Mr Beckford's tower and I fear that I will not be able to relate faithfully this experience for I know not where to begin. The distant spire of Salisbury Cathedral appears amongst woodland although I know that not to be the case but there are many tree tops between these two landmarks. Salisbury Plain is conspicuous enough and where this chalk mass rises up I could see many flocks of sheep grazing in small clusters and the gentle parched green folds of the Plain extend to a hazy horizon where clouds gathered. I continued my circuit of the octagonal room and enquired of my guide as to the location of a further tower and he replied without venturing to the window; "That would be King Alfred's tower at Stourhead Sur". Indeed this conspicuous building aided my eventual approach to the Stourhead Inn and I intend to ascend that structure also. Of a sudden I felt the desire to fall from this great height and as quickly as this strange feeling entered my thoughts and turned my stomach over it then departed. With the shock of this notion of self murder I took a pace back from the window but I believe now that it is a trick of the mind when it makes for itself that unimaginable thought. I felt a deal more cautious for the remainder of my viewing from this position but was determined to overcome this foolishness. A movement caught my eye and I followed the course of a large brown bird as it sailed closely beneath me in the warm afternoon air with barely a twitch of its great ragged wings. I am certain that this most regal of species would have expended even less effort had it not been pursued by two smaller angry black birds that I believe to be crows. I took one last look below at the building itself, at the

industry involved in its creation and at the grounds
that display great variety with a determination to
avoid any regularity or conspicuous plan. I have not
yet visited the alpine regions but I believe that the
author and artist of these surrounds has borrowed
from his travels for it is not England that has been his
inspiration. My guide shuffled politely in the centre
of the room and I gestured that we should reunite with
terra firma for both our sakes to which he needed
little encouragement. As we descended slowly and
with caution I realised that I had indeed fulfilled my
wager although I had no proof other than my word. I
revealed this matter to my guide who begged my
pardon and informed me that it was his duty to escort
me back to await Mr Beckford in his chambers. I
regretted that this was not my intention and that I
must depart for fear of causing more confusion than
currently existed. The poor gentleman was all of a
quiver in his dilemma as he dared not fail in his duty.
At length he told me that it was more than his life was
worth but he would report that I had fled from his
company into the grounds and then suggested in
hushed tones that a team of wagons were due to depart

for Hindon shortly. I apologised sincerely for making his situation troublesome and he led me to a much humbler exit than that of my entrance to this place and I made my hasty departure.

As my guide had indicated the wagons were mustering and I slipped aboard at the rear of one vehicle where the dusty workforce appeared to be in a condition of intoxicated oblivion and were altogether ignorant of my presence. I looked back as we made our slow retreat from that fantastic structure and I make no pretence that I was in some fear of reprisal and wished myself away from this place as swiftly as possible. I kept my vigil as the wagon rumbled on and this attention was fully justified as I spied a figure on horseback, who in a short while would intercept our course and I soon established that it was the diminutive servant on a toy white steed. As we passed between vegetation I quietly slipped from the back of the lumbering wagon and pushed my way into the darkness of the evergreen woodland and crouched down from view. The rider hailed for the driver to halt and my pursuer rode around the open wagon inspecting each weary and grimy face in turn until I heard the course rasp of instruction to the driver to continue. The little man then turned his pony towards my position and skirted the edge of the woodland and I held up my hands before my face but could not resist to peek between my fingers as he passed close by. His face was screwed up in anger and he mouthed unprintable obscenities until he spied another wagon departing from the Abbey and he then dug in his heels and galloped to inspect its passengers. I lay back in my position of concealment and with my head resting on my pack I must have passed into sleep for when I looked next the light was failing and dusk had crept in as a grey smoke gently drifting across the parkland. On awaking I sensed my dreadful hunger and remembered the roadside apples that I had collected and I drank deeply from my water flask before continuing on my way. In time this track led to a gatehouse where I could hear hounds snarling and barking, a sound which sent my heart racing and as silently as I was able, I approached the closed gates. A light flickered in the window of the lodge and I gently drew up the heavy iron bar which fastened the gate as the first of the dogs appeared from the rear of the small house. The heat of panic was upon me and as I tried to squeeze through the narrow opening that I had made the pack on my back then caught for a moment but before the snarling hounds were upon me I was able to pass between the gates and drop the bar back into place. I then rolled from view behind the stone gate pillar as the slavering dogs hit the slatted gate as one and sensing my close proximity they continued their noise and displayed their vicious teeth with wild eyed frustration. Having released these guard dogs the Gatekeeper followed behind and mercifully, being unaware of my presence, he then set about them with a stick and snarled his own instruction for them to disperse into the parkland within the great wall. I stood with my back to the gatepost, breathing deeply and thankful that I had made my exit and that I was not still at large within the grounds of Fonthill Abbey.

My writing hand is near seized in its position around my pen and I must halt and rest. I shall also take some air for this is a place most worthy of exploration and unlike the lair of the Caliph of Fonthill, visitors are made welcome to the grounds

and garden of Stourhead and also to the house itself.
My Dear Uncle, I include a letter to myself from Mr
Richard Fenton that I received on my arrival at the
Stourhead Inn which explains much. I fear that I have
not the time or energy to transcribe it as I have more
of my own adventure to relate but if you are able to
read Mr Fenton's hand you will find that it confirms
my status as a guest of Sir Richard Colt Hoare for the
duration of my stay at this Inn. It is an act of
generosity for which I am truly grateful and I am
honoured that I shall be able to thank my host in
person.

Wednesday 14th October

Dear Mr Henry Chalk

It was with great alarm that I learnt of the challenge
and wager that was made between yourself and my son
Mr John Fenton at the George Inn on the evening of
the 13th of October and I have scolded him for such a
foolish action although he claims that it was made in
jest after much libation. I suggest that you embarked
upon a wager that you could not possibly afford to lose
for my son has informed me that when he entered your
room you were cleaning your own boots at a saving of

perhaps 6d which can only indicate a condition of severe impecuniosity. I regretted your absence at dinner and believed your ailment to be genuine and I sincerely hope that you are recovered yet I have a suspicion also that your lack of funds prompted an early retirement to your room when you were without question a guest at our table.

Sir Richard Colt Hoare shares my concern at your ill advised venture as any uninvited approach to the dark domain of Fonthill Abbey is certain to end in failure as Mr Beckford is not one to entertain the casual or the curious visitor and there are real dangers attached to such a mission. Sir Richard has made arrangements with the staff at the Stourhead Inn to welcome you as his guest for the duration of your stay and extends an invitation for you to make your acquaintance with the Baronet at Stourhead House.

Your presence will be anticipated at the House in due course and Mr John Fenton will be on hand to make his apology to you in person.

Your anxious and faithful friend

Richard Fenton

It is now evening and I have just eaten the best
meal since my arrival in this county of which I must
neglect in offering an account. How can a traveller
relate all his tales as I am attempting when an equal
proportion of time appears necessary to both the
experience and the documentation. Perhaps my Dear
Uncle I have mistaken my worth as a correspondent
and these letters are now received with a sense of
dread. I know not how long I shall remain at this
location for I should welcome any news of your own to
redress this flow of correspondence as it floods from
my pen.

It was too dark to consult my map and the
Stourhead Inn was a distant goal that I had not the
strength in my limbs to attempt for I felt hollow with
hunger. I drained the remaining water from my flask
and shuddered at the howls of the murderous pack as
they patrolled that forbidden territory within the
fortified walls of Fonthill Estate and I then followed
the road downhill. I thought no further than spending
the night in a barn or stable but encountered no such
opportunity and in time I found myself entering a
village where I thought I might find a simple Inn and

part with my few remaining pennies for the sake of a bed for the night. There were indeed many Inns in this place for it was a coaching station and I soon established that this busy village was called Hindon which was the location for the parliamentary election that Mr Beckford had referred to. There was every sign of the bacchanalian excess that the prospective candidate so abhorred with fellows lurching about the high street calling and jeering and swilling from bottles and there were other poor souls at a more advanced stage of celebration who were simply lying still in the gutter. A fire had been lit in the centre of the road which prospered from all manner of election detritus with placards, rough benches and the election hustings tossed in to feed this haphazard conflagration. A small fire engine had been employed to squirt water at this blaze to ensure its containment yet even the operators of this device had been smitten by the all pervading sickness of the election process as they lurched and stumbled wildly in the execution of their pumping duties. Somewhere amongst this bedlam of parliamentary procedure Mr Beckford's representative was at large and I clung to the shadows

as best I could for I did not relish a further encounter.
I asked discreetly at a number of Inns for a night's
lodging but election fever had ensured that there was
not a bed to be found in the place. I was drawn to a
brazier and I purchased some hot chestnuts from a
boy for twopence and I received them in a twist of old
news and set about prizing open the blackened shells
to gain access to the steaming treasure inside. This
was welcome food indeed but I became aware that my
actions were being observed by a stranger and as our
eyes met across the wavering heat of the brazier I felt
a shiver pass through my body as I sensed a
malevolent intent behind this man's unfaltering stare
and I slowly withdrew from the fire's glow and began a
retreat back into the shadows. I looked behind me
and this short and stout character had left the brazier
also and now followed me downhill at a distance. My
Dear Uncle, the situation soon worsened for
approaching me and coming up the street were three
figures with one holding aloft a lantern and the person
in the middle, who was wearing a tall hat, was half the
size of those on each flank and I knew in an instant
that it was Mr Beckford's diminutive servant. A

course bark from that little fellow told me that recognition had been mutual and I felt too drained of my strength and my ankle not sufficiently healed to outrun any pursuer. Fortune was with me as I sensed that a narrow gap existed between two large stone built houses and I slipped off my pack and stepped sideways between the stonework not knowing what lay ahead of me in the darkness. With my chest compressed in this limited space I was barely able to breathe as I pushed on and I could just find room to turn my head to look behind and for a moment the stout man from the brazier looked on before his form was replaced by the illumination of the lamp thrust in between the buildings. I could clearly see the snarl on the little servant's face as he observed me and he then growled to his henchmen that he wanted me apprehended to; "Teach that boy a lesson". The only person capable of pursuit was clearly attired for more important duties and both henchmen protested that they were unable to follow my route due to their size although an attempt was made and one man was soon lodged firmly between the stonework and shrieked like a pig to be hauled free. This was surely no passageway but simply two buildings that did not touch and I squeezed out into a small yard and returning to darkness I climbed walls and fences with the fear that danger waited for me at every turn and I was determined that I should escape this h*** on earth. However hard I tried I could not find a way to open country and I was soon back in the yard of another inn and I heard again that course voice out in the street beyond the arch. My will was broken and I felt too weak to attempt a further blind stumbling amongst the rear of these properties and I was now fully prepared to meet my pursuers and accept any consequences that were due to me however painful and unpleasant they may be. As I walked towards the street and in the shadows of the archway I met with a figure and begged their pardon as we had made contact in the darkness. I could smell a fresh flowery scent that was at odds with this dreadful place and I said "Excuse me Madam". I was taken aback by the response of this young woman for she was clearly in distress. "Sir, I fear for my safety in this place, please can you help me?". I could hear Mr Beckford's servant approaching as he made further demands of his men to seek me out. "Madam" I replied "I will certainly help you but I too am in some danger and there is little time to explain". The young lady's voice was filled with uncertainty, "Sir, I hope and believe I can trust you, please act swiftly for both our sakes. Will you please take my arm." I assured the young lady that I was to be trusted and that I would explain all once it was safe to do so. I then guided her to the yard where I had a moment before passed a stationary carriage and I ran my hand along its side until I found the door handle. I slipped off my pack and tossed it ahead of me with my stick and once inside I offered to lift up the young lady with both hands and she first handed me her own stick and also a paper parcel, I then ensured that she was sitting comfortably on the seat before quietly closing the carriage door. I heard the little mans boots on the cobbles as he approached the carriage and he then struck its wheel. " . . . And in here," he demanded. "But I done 'im earlier Mister Pierro" protested the henchman, "Again, I go to take my place at the 'ead of the table, come find me when you get im."

The boots retreated and we listened to the underling grumbling to himself," Yous' jes a stinkin'

dwarf is all you is n' Mistur Beckford kin rot in
****". We heard the door to the inn open and close
with a brief burst of the bacchanalian excess within
and we then sat listening to our own breathing inside
the darkness of the coach. How long we sat in silence
I do not know but in time I whispered that I felt that
we were safe to talk and I introduced myself and
apologised for my clandestine behaviour. The young
lady introduced herself and I shall refer to her as Miss
Foster for I do not wish to compromise her propriety,
indeed this was not a usual situation in finding
ourselves alone together but it was a circumstance
that could not be anticipated. I asked whether I
should now be allowed to escort Miss Foster back to
her lodging but she responded that it appeared unsafe
to venture from our current security and that we
should wait a while longer. Miss Foster then asked
quietly whether I was now at liberty to explain my
own predicament as I had at first promised and I was
relieved to notice that the distress had now left her
voice. I answered truthfully that I knew not where to
start and she advised me that as with any story, I
should start at the beginning and so My Dear Uncle I

found myself again on the roof of the Exeter stage all those days ago. In the darkness I listened to my own voice as it trailed the route of my excursion and I found that I could not exclude the details of the loss of my purse or the warmth of my feelings for Peter Winter and the boy Tam. There was also no omission of the antics of Mr John Fenton although these were thoughts and feelings that I had not even voiced to myself. Miss Foster wanted to hear every detail of my uninvited excursion to Fonthill Abbey and she knew not that such places existed in this world. I related that Mr James Wyatt, the architect of that building, had referred to the sugar market and I believed that Mr Beckford's great wealth had been accrued in this way. Miss Foster spoke of her sadness about this cruel trade as slavery was at the heart of that business. I confessed to knowing little about the subject but I was assured that it was a matter about which her family held very strong views. There was a great sincerity to her voice as she spoke about this evil to mankind and that Mr Beckford was surely the worst kind of man and Fonthill Abbey a monument to inhumanity and she informed me that she was raised to always speak out about such an injustice. I felt myself recoil inside my own ignorance as this young lady then lectured me on our nation's history and as a pioneer of the trading in slaves we have much to be ashamed of. The people of this country though have won the day and our Government has been made to follow with the passing this year into law of the Bill to abolish the entire British slave trade. Miss Foster then showed curiosity as to whether I indeed followed the affairs of the world at all? I confessed that I was not accustomed to reading newspapers and knew very little of interest other than perhaps a few dusty facts that were of no consequence to anyone. This young lady however appeared my antithesis and seemed quite at ease with the affairs of Government, war and reform and she also assured me that she had never read a single newspaper but instead enjoyed the learned company of her family where discussion on all matters was encouraged. Miss Foster then urged me not to consider her as one with only strong and serious views as she also held an appreciation for music and the theatre and above all she considered that laughter was the greatest panacea. For my part my Dear Uncle I did not know how to proceed with this dialogue for I have no experience of such encounters with the opposite sex and Miss Foster appeared so forthright in her manner. I recalled the book that I have read a portion of on my travels "A Sentimental Journey" and for want of any other subject I could bring to mind I asked of Miss Foster whether she had read this work. I at once knew it to be inappropriate but could not retract my question from the darkness and she at once demanded to hear of it. My voice stumbled and I apologised that I had mentioned it for I now considered that its content was improper. Miss Foster replied boldly; "I am not so delicate that I may faint at the slightest indelicacy and I should like to hear of it". I could find no exit from this situation and I suggested that I had a short candle in my pack and I could light it with which to read. The young lady was quick to oppose this action lest the men should return and instead proposed that I should recall it as best I could for it must still be fresh in my mind. I cleared my throat and paused to gather the threads of this strange tale. I explained that the hero of this little volume was Yorrick and he travelled with no objective through France other than to cross paths with beautiful women and indeed from the narrative you would believe that little else existed in that country. There are many distractions along the way and I recalled how Yorrick requires guidance to the Opera Comique and passes a dozen shops until his eye settles upon someone he considers worthy of interruption from their business to supply these directions. In a glove shop he spies the "Beautiful Grisset" whom he engages in conversation and from the doorstep of her shop she patiently tells him which streets to take to find the Opera Comique. Yorrick then repeated his thanks as many times as her instructions and then reluctantly departs only to find that he has not gone ten paces before he fully forgets every word that the Beautiful Grisset has uttered. He then returns and with great boldness offers the excuse that "tis possible, replied I, when a man is thinking more of a woman than of her good advice". I advised Miss Foster that the situation grows worse for the shopkeeper invites Yorrick into her shop for she has a delivery boy soon to depart in our hero's intended direction if the gentleman would like to wait. They enter the shop and I know not how he contrives it for in a moment Yorrick is sitting beside the Beautiful Grisset and has her delicate hand within his and he is feeling her pulse." I stopped the narrative at this point for I felt I had already related too much of this tale which appeared all the more full of scandal now I was hearing it in my own words. Miss Foster then demanded to know what happened next to the hero Yorrick and the beautiful Grisset and I had to inform her that the husband then appeared in the shop at that very moment to which I heard a short gasp by the young lady. Her shock was short lived for she soon began to laugh and perhaps out of my own nervous condition I too began to laugh, at the narrative, at our situation as two strangers sitting within a stationary carriage and at the loss of my senses within this darkness. Miss Foster then calmed her laughter and asked me in earnest "And what would the hero of your tale make of my pulse?" I knew not how to answer her request other than to say that I felt certain that it would be a situation to his liking for it had all the correct requirements; an implausible excuse, an intimacy with a young woman who is also a stranger and a scene set in a carriage that is going nowhere at all. I remembered the chestnuts that had grown cold in their newspaper wrapping and offered this suggestion to Miss Foster. At first she made no reply and in the black interior I could sense my own pulse beating at my wrist and bounding through my heart and at my temples. An eternity passed before she calmly revealed that in the package she was carrying were apples and some bread that she had intended to feed to the horses and indeed that was her purpose for straying from her room. I fumbled for the package on the seat where I had tossed it and then tore and ate the bread for it could not have been more welcome. Miss Foster then informed me of her own circumstances and that she was travelling with her Brother Robert and they could only find one room on this the busiest of nights. Her Brother had assured her that he would find somewhere to reside even if it was on a table and despite her protests he had left his sister to enable her to retire for the night on the understanding that she would under no circumstances stray from her room. Miss Foster felt ashamed that she had not heeded her Brother's advice but she found that she could not sleep for the noise in this place and confessed to a great fondness for horses and felt a desire to feed that most worthy and friendly of animals. Whilst I ate she told me of her great admiration for her Brother and then introduced me to her family life and her anticipation at being soon reunited after their visit to London. Miss Foster spoke of her pleasure and experiences of London Life and in her short stay she knew more of the heart of the place than I and I confessed to being a cosseted resident. She then talked at length of this and that and in time she sighed and made a wish; " I do not want this one night to end for daybreak will bring this ugly place back on to its knees and we have travelled in our carriage to a special destination that I have never before visited . . . ". I could not answer and in that pause Miss Foster bowed her head and made her own response, "It has already happened, has it not?" Pale and uninvited the beginnings of the new day had crept into our carriage and my night was over and in this callow light I could see that Miss Foster was without sight. She was indeed more beautiful than I ever imagined throughout our passage in darkness and now the dawn had conspired to tell of her secret. She smiled and spoke softly "So Mr Chalk, you have the advantage of me and do you not consider that we have been on equal terms and should remain so until our journey is truly over and we leave this carriage?" Miss Foster gently raised her hands before her and I positioned myself so that she could easily find her target. Tenderly she first ran her fingers around the outline of my face to gauge its shape and then explored the interior from the line of my hair to the eyes and cheekbones all the while reading with her fingertips these contours until she traced my nose downwards to my lips. There her hands fell away and she requested that I should escort her back to her room.

My Dear Uncle I am truly exhausted with the telling of the events of this day and night. Before my pen drops to the floor I would request that if you discard, neglect or light your fire with my scraps of correspondence I hope and pray that you will safeguard these last few pages for this shall be a memory that I will endeavour to retain but that one day I might be reminded of its every detail. Before I have a second thought about dispatching this most intimate of accounts I shall seal this letter and I pray you will not be offended by its content as there is surely a hope that honesty shall win the day over any suggestion of impropriety.

This pedestrian tourist, having returned Miss Foster to her room, took a long drink of water from the pump and then stepped over the squalid remnants of yesterdays parliamentary election; the bodies, the limp bunting and the smouldering benches and banners and I do not recall my feet making contact with terra firma again until I reached my destination, the Stourhead Inn, and neither do I recall a single detail along the way.

Goodnight or Good morning, My Dear Uncle, for I know not which applies.

Your persistent Nephew,
HENRY CHALK.

Friday 16th October 1807

My Dear Uncle,

This morning I found difficulty in raising myself from my fine bed and I shall not tell you of what hour I took my breakfast. I find I have still not awoken fully and I cannot break the circle of lifting myself from the chair and going to the window, rubbing hard at my sore eyes with tight fists and then returning to my chair. I have a callous on my finger from its contact with the pen for which I have only myself to blame and my mind feels like the struggle of an injured pedestrian tourist for I cannot put one thought in front of the other. All the while I have in my grasp a piece of paper that has on it a name and address written in my own hand and it is the only proof I have that my encounter at Hindon was not a cruel but beautiful dream. I have an appointment to keep with Mr Richard Fenton and an invitation to make the acquaintance of Sir Richard Colt Hoare at

Stourhead House and I wonder that I am not in a more healthy state of anticipation.

The day has now passed and I can report my Dear Uncle that although I did finally manage to escape the comfort of my room I am installed once again in my chair with pen and callous reunited.

After making myself as presentable as a walking tourist's wardrobe would permit I made the short journey up the hill to Stourhead House. There is an attractive twin towered gatehouse through which you make your approach to the Baronet's home. Beyond this archway there stands an orderly line of fine sweet chestnut trees that I can recognise from the curious twisting of its bark as it spirals up the girth of the trunk and also by the littering of its produce on the lawn below with the splits in these spiky green cases revealing the glinting darkness of its seed. The house has a grand façade and a neat symmetry, but what do I know of such places save to say it is pleasing to the eye? There is a large expanse of parkland before the house and then level ground beyond which ceases with a range of hills and evidence of earthen banks or ancient fortifications at the summit of this abrupt ridge. It is indeed appropriate that the author of this county's ancient history should have this visible daily reminder of prehistoric occupation occurring on his doorstep. I judged that I could also see the tower of Fonthill Abbey and the strangeness of that place sends a chill down my back and it seems that it is a landmark that shall haunt me for eternity. There was a succession of tourists approaching and entering the house and I followed behind and then announced my presence to the footman. I was informed that Sir Richard and his guests were shooting today and I was for departing but it appeared that the public were quite at liberty to inspect the place and this was a fact confirmed by the footman and so I became myself a house tourist for the afternoon. In this fine and spacious entrance hall there is barely a section of wall that is not covered with a painting and I suspect that many of these faces that loom from their dark backgrounds are ancestors and members of the Baronets family. I overheard a member of the staff addressing one small group of observers and pointing out a representation of Sir Richard Colt Hoare and his son. I waited for the party to continue before I took my position beneath this heavy gilt frame. Sir Richard has a gentle countenance and also a detectable sadness and while the son seems keen to explore beyond the confines of the painting the father is preoccupied with his portfolio of antiquarian studies and seems reluctant to leave his position. I found myself reflecting on my own Father's refusal to submit to my childish whims as if it were a display of weakness to revisit those feelings of playfulness from ones youth. I heard a voice speaking aloud these very thoughts and I was taken aback to recognise it as my own; "Go with your son and leave those encumbrances that build walls around yourself". I quickly looked about me to ensure that this advice to the Master of the house had passed unnoticed and I need not have concerned myself for I was soon overtaken by a very vocal lady and her entourage. I followed this group at a distance and it soon became apparent that very little here at Stourhead House met with her high expectations and a display of appreciation or condemnation was proclaimed most publicly. I wonder that the owners of these country houses admit such critical tourists for this lady was

keen to list the many other large establishments to
which she had gained admittance and how Wilton
House was "Too grand, too gloomy" and even
regarding the surrounds here at Stourhead "I cannot
think it equal to a situation in our own
neighbourhood". As the party confronted each
painting in turn the male escort would look to this
lady arbiter of good taste before offering any hint as to
his own views on the matter lest it should be for when
it should be against and vice versa. The prima critic
even adopted the cunning means of hinting at her
feelings and then would playfully change her course
in the opposing direction once the unfortunate
gentleman had mustered the courage to voice an
observation. "No, no, no Mr James it may be well
executed but it is most certainly NOT hung to its best
advantage" This poor fellow would then retreat to the
rear of the party and keep his silence, I suspect, for
the remainder of the excursion. The most curious
object encountered was a heavily ornamented cabinet
that once belonged to Pope Sixtus and I cannot say
My Dear Uncle whether it is to be attributed to good
taste or consigned to bad for at this stage of the

proceedings I had thankfully parted company with the critical tourists. It is old and it is odd is all I know and I fear for the male entourage once they are obliged to pass judgement on this unique piece of furniture for whatever they propose will result in apoplexy and, I am certain, receive a withering response from their female Cicero. There are a number of small paintings here by John Robert Cozens that I favour if I have to show my preference which I am glad to say I am under no obligation to do. I then left the house and sought out the tower which is perhaps a distance of a mile or so and I found it strange to walk without Peter Winter's stick which I now fully associate with walking any distance at all and neither did I have my pack on my back to which I have become so accustomed. On this fine and clear afternoon I instead carried a burden of a much weightier variety for there is only one subject to which my thoughts constantly return and I fear that I shall soon be driven to madness by this turmoil. I am perpetually required to gather my senses and return them to the task of observation but I may as well be in the streets of Stockwell, Paris or Calcutta rather than

the environs of Stourhead House. A human being is a
curious thing for on the exterior of it we are all busy
with some activity and even a crowd of this species
can appear to have a single purpose yet inside we are
all churning away at our own thoughts. Today, my
Dear Uncle, I can report that I have successfully
manufactured some fine Wiltshire butter where
previously I had a rational mind.

King Alfred's Tower stands one hundred and sixty
feet high and such was my preoccupation I very
nearly stumbled into the sheer brick sides of the
place. There could not be a better remedy for my
pathetic ailment than ascending these one hundred
and sixty feet in near darkness to then be exposed to
the brilliance of the day at the summit and I believe
that this is the calculated effect and purpose of such a
structure. The body savours the conclusion of this
endeavour and the reward is total for we are now
united with the sky and all earthly matters are left two
hundred and twenty two steps beneath our feet. I was
content to gulp great volumes of fresh air to fill my
lungs before unravelling the patchwork blanket of the
countryside below. There are but three sides to this

tower compared to the eight of Fonthill and although the elevation may not be as great at Stourhead the position of this structure commands a greater view to the west as the land falls away in that direction. Fonthill Abbey again demands the attention with Salisbury Cathedral a faint but discernible landmark and looking to the west there is a pimple rising from a flat plain with a building at its apex which I am informed is Glastonbury Tor which lies in the heart of the county of Somerset.

There is a significance with the positioning of this tower which has everything to do with the activities of our ancient Monarch King Alfred who fought and defeated the Danes in 879 AD and his march to battle passed this very spot and his deeds are rightfully remembered by this erection. It is indeed fortunate that our Royal ancestor passed this way as I believe that there could not be a more suitable location for observing the manner in which this land changes. The great hub of chalk that forms the bulk of South Wiltshire finally comes to an end, at perhaps its most westerly point, and I have already referred to the signs of prehistoric occupation that perch on this final chalk crest and are evident from the front door of Stourhead House. At the foot of the termination of this chalk there lies a broad flat area that is largely under cultivation until a further ridge is met on which line King Alfred's Tower stands and there is a large tract of woodland where oak trees appear to flourish. With this further step down to the west which is coincident with the meeting of the adjacent counties of Somerset, Dorset and Wiltshire there could not be a more natural division for it is determined by the changing nature of the land itself. Somerset and the west is a place of small fields contained by thick hedges and there is a sense of lushness and I can detect water glistening in the afternoon sun where it has settled in the cart rutted trackways and drainage ditches. There is a parched dryness to the chalk hills to the east and I wonder that this holding of the water on the land has much to do with the nature of the soil itself and the earth below.

Having found a place of sanctuary for my troubled mind I spent a good hour on the roof of this elevation and in that time a number of visitors huffed and puffed and then departed. A boy of perhaps nine or

ten ascended with his Father and proceeded to
furnish me with more details than I can now recall
about the tower and indeed it was he that informed me
of the height and the number of steps that we had to
traverse to reach the summit. This youth was fairly
effervescent with facts for he then numbered the
amount of bricks required to build King Alfred's
Tower as near on one million. I asked whether he had
made a count of them all to which this resource of
information finally dried up and the Father who had
been silently observing the enthusiasm of his
offspring owned up to having read the eager child a
pamphlet on the subject. This gentleman then
continued to relate the remainder of the details
regarding the structure itself and that these million
red bricks were manufactured near to this very spot
and we then discussed the changing nature of the
ground hereabouts that yielded brick earth or clay
suitable for the manufacture of such fine bricks.
Before the Father and Son departed we introduced
ourselves and I can inform you that their names are
Mr Charles Brown and Master James Brown and they
reside in the town of Frome in Somerset and indeed

Master Brown pointed to the cluster of distant buildings as proof of the existence of that place. With the roof again vacated I patrolled its three sides for a final inspection and observed for some minutes the progress of a team of horses drawing a plough across a field of stubble. There was surely some satisfaction to be gained from this procedure by the ploughman, this visible record of control and accuracy left in his wake after each passing with the dramatic change from dull weathered crust to dark freshly broken soil. A straggle of white birds followed this slow excavation to reap its immediate reward as they descended onto this disturbed ground directly after the plough had done its work, seeking which soil born creature I wonder other than the earth worm? By their actions I believe these to be sea birds and the simple worm must be a rich delicacy indeed to draw these feeders from the distant coast and all the fruits of the sea.

I then descended the two hundred and twenty steps fearing that my mind would again resume its former turmoil once my feet made contact with the earths' surface but I am pleased to report that the prescription of elevation and fresh air has had its good effect. On a scrap of paper I have made a drawing of the tower for it is an impressive monument and a conspicuous landmark. I then drifted back to my lodgings, not assiduously observing everything in my wake nor churning butter in my head but a pleasant nothingness existed between King Alfred's Tower and the Stourhead Inn. On my return I received a note from Mr Richard Fenton apologising for their absence today but tomorrow a barrow opening is arranged and I should be welcome to Stourhead House after breakfast has been taken. I have sent a note of acceptance to this kind offer and now for a while I am content to enjoy a good coal fire in my room before I again put pen to paper and you will be relieved to learn my Dear Uncle that it is, for once, a correspondence that is not heading in your direction.

Your faithful and bewildered Nephew,
HENRY CHALK

Saturday 17th October 1807

MY DEAR UNCLE,

Another day has passed and how they pass! I am
again sitting before the burning coals and I have a fug
in my head which I hope will clear as I proceed. At
breakfast I received a letter, the very sight of which
sent my heart leaping yet the contents could not have
had a more unsettling effect. This correspondence
arrived from Hindon and it is in the hand of Miss
Foster's Brother, Mr Robert Foster whom I have not
met, yet he has been charged with the responsibility
of conveying the warm and gentle thoughts of his Dear
sister as it is a task which she will never be able to
undertake. In addition Mr Robert Foster has
corresponded on his own behalf, in part to express his
concern at his Sister's foolish excursion from the
safety of her room but also expressing the firm trust
that he places in his Dear Sister's judgement as to the
character of the one whom came to her aid. The

author then gives an account of the events of that same evening which explain much and have shocked me greatly. Indeed there could not be a greater distance between good and evil on one page with the former news all grace and beauty and the latter unthinkable in its darkness and danger. Sir, it is sufficient for me to inform you that Mr Robert Foster could not fail to overhear a loud and drunken soliloquy from Mr William Beckford's diminutive servant, delivered whilst his head was resting on the election table. At that time Mr Robert Foster knew not of the characters or circumstance to which this little man referred until the next morning when brother and sister were again united. The small man's utterings made it clear that an intruder had entered the Fonthill Abbey grounds and at the great door to that place had been mistaken for another by this same servant and admitted into the building itself. Indeed for his culpability in propagating this misunderstanding the miniature domestic had then received a severe beating from his master. It is apparent that the intruder's visit coincided with the long anticipated arrival of another, not dissimilar in age or appearance to myself, for whom Mr William Beckford has, "an unspeakable and fundamental interest". I am not so sheltered from the ways of the world that I cannot understand to what Mr Robert Foster is referring and I have been sworn not to repeat any hint of this odious matter to his dear sister. I wished to banish the worst of these thoughts from my mind yet treasure the remainder and such was this mix of feelings that it spun my head around as I approached Stourhead House to meet its Master, Sir Richard Colt Hoare. On my arrival Mr Richard Fenton took one look at my countenance and realised that all was not as it should have been and set me down, calling at once for a large brandy. I could not explain my turmoil nor did Mr Fenton attempt to establish the cause of my palpable suffering but was content to put me at my ease and offer his kind assurances which in combination with the brandy did indeed straighten my senses. I was soon able to present myself to the Baronet who could not have shown more sincerity in his welcome and I confirmed that I was in eager anticipation of the antiquarian activities in the day ahead. I thanked him also for his kind generosity in arranging my accommodation at the Stourhead Inn but it appeared a matter that he regarded as of little consequence and he shook his head gently. Mr Fenton was on hand to rescue this brief awkwardness and he assured me that his son was to appear shortly to make his apology for the incorrect and injudicious wager that was made at the George Inn at Amesbury. I was ordered to take my seat in this fine drawing room and I knew that I could not divulge any part of my tale without explanation of the whole and so I resolved to say nothing on the matter and I was content for the present company to judge that I had not been successful in my appointed task. Mr Richard Fenton stated that there was ever only going to be one outcome to such an impossible challenge and he expressed his delight at my safe return. At this point Mr John Fenton appeared and he greeted me warmly and appeared to show a genuine remorse as we shook hands and he offered me a comprehensive apology for the foolishness of his actions. I confirmed that I was determined to settle with him the full sum of our wager when circumstances permitted as my financial situation and impecuniosity now appeared to be common knowledge within the present company. At this point Mr Richard Fenton leapt to his feet and interjected most forcibly as he addressed me "Sir, you will do no such thing. It is my Son that is at fault and it is he who should fully compensate for his mischief and the suffering caused to yourself that we have indeed been witness to on this very morning. What say you John?" The younger Mr Fenton then rose from his seat to say his piece; "I agree Sir and offer again my unequivocal apology to Mr Chalk and so Father as you are the holder of my allowance and as a consequence are therefore my banker I request Sir that a sum of the full cost of the original wager is paid immediately to the unfortunate young gentleman without delay" Mr John Fenton then sat down and it was the turn of Mr Richard Fenton to twist and turn and pat at his pockets with some uncertainty until Sir Richard Colt Hoare who looked on with a sign of mild amusement on his face then gestured for Mr Fenton to sit down and cease his fluster. He then quietly assured all present that to see an end to this increasingly unseemly muddle he would see to it that wager was settled in my favour and that they could now turn their attentions to the important issues of the day which were purely of an antiquarian nature. I opened my mouth in protest as I did not see for one moment why Sir Richard should be inconvenienced in this way but I was silenced by a firm glance from the Baronet as if to say that really was the end of the matter. Later in the afternoon on our return to Stourhead House the steward presented me with a purse containing five guineas which I had no option but to gratefully receive. I resolved then to repay this kind gesture when time permits.

We then departed from Stourhead House and made our way in the carriage to the crest of the chalk downs, I was in eager anticipation of my activity with the pick and shovel as there was a damp chill in the air and I had determined that barrow excavation would be warming work indeed. I cannot pretend, my Dear Uncle, that I was disappointed to discover that this undertaking was well in advance as two labourers had already been employed to the task and it seems the timing of our arrival had been judged accordingly to witness their near completion. I was introduced to

the two Mr Parkers, Steven and John, who are a team
of Father and Son and are Mr William Cunnington's
men and I am informed that they have performed the
opening of many hundred of these sacred burial
mounds under the guidance of that same gentleman.
To my mind no greater care seemed to be exercised as
with the digging of any hole, ditch, well or indeed
anywhere that there was a deal of soil to shift. The
expected object, or "primary interment" can be
predicted to exist at the original turf level where a
"cist" or small hole has been dug into the native
chalk. This would have occurred at the origin of the
barrow and into this depression the body or the
cremated remains of the occupant would be lain and
perhaps, in the case of the latter, a crude pottery urn
is often the preferred vessel. The mound itself would
then be created above the burial as the surrounding
ground was excavated and then heaped up into the
centre leaving an outer ditch from whence this raised
material had been borrowed. I believe at their initial
creation these domes in the landscape would not form
part of the green sward as they do today but would be
white beacons of glistening chalk and from their

prominent positions would present extraordinary landmarks. I thought back to yesterday and my hour spent aloft at the top of King Alfred's Tower when I had wondered at the natural division of the land here where this great bulk of chalk in South Wiltshire finally plunges down before the boundary with the county of Somerset is met. In ancient times a traveller coming from the west would leave the wet lands behind him and witness the unfamiliar dryness of this elevated chalk country. A gleaming white barrow on the crest of the ridge would call out to this stranger from the west "We are the chalk people and we live at the beginning and at the end of the chalk world". I wondered how this stranger would be met and what trade would he make with these occupants? The barrow that was currently undergoing the attentions of the pick and the shovel is perhaps not the earliest landmark on this ridge for it is positioned on the edge of a circle which Sir Richard Colt Hoare has determined, from the faintness of its vallum, as that of high antiquity. I walked the circumference of this ancient ring that would have at one time in the history of this place also have presented its bright whiteness

to the west before the passage of time had subdued
the virgin chalk and the grazing beast trampled its
form. It is a circle of small proportions when
compared to the gargantuan Yarnbury Castle or
indeed to the fort that exists not a half a mile from this
very spot on this same ridge with its bold banks and
ditches where its defensive purpose is plain for all to
see. What purpose then for a circle that is not a
fortress yet commands the same aspect as its
neighbour? I wished to confirm with the Baronet that
the burial mound was indeed of a later date than this
circle on which it had been so blatantly positioned yet
on the near completion of my circuit I was urged to
hurry by Mr Richard Fenton to rejoin our small group
to witness an important stage in the antiquarian
ceremony. The barrow from which the two Mr Parkers
had ably disgorged such great volumes of this chalk
now finally relinquished its content for our cursory
inspection and a single skeleton was revealed with not
an urn or single artefact to accompany this lonely
occupant. A signal was given to the two perspiring
labourers to reverse this operation and our party retired
to the shelter of the carriage where refreshments were

on hand and the circulation of the bottle kept a warm glow upon this high exposure. Indeed the antics of the two Mr Fentons kept us in amusement also with John producing a flute on which he performed with no small amount of skill and his father then sang a song which demonstrated his Cambrian origins. In time we were interrupted by the tapping of Mr Steven Parker on the carriage door who having heaved the spoil back into position on the initial barrow had now, as instructed, set to work upon one of the three smaller examples that lay on the very crest of Whitesheet Hill. We were informed that a skeleton had been unearthed and we then left the sanctuary of the carriage and made our way across to the barrow closest to the edge of the slope with Mr Richard Fenton approaching the heap of freshly spewed chalk on tippy toes in a most theatrical manner. On peering into the excavation and observing the skull he then threw his hands up and cried out; "It grinned horribly a ghastly smile" and indeed the visage of this unfortunate occupant presented a most unsettling sight.

I confess my Dear Uncle that after a large brandy in the morning and a turn or two of the circulating

bottle I felt very weary and it was suggested that I
should rest a while in the carriage and indeed I fell
fully asleep and only awoke on our return to
Stourhead House. I apologised profusely to Sir
Richard Colt Hoare and I found him to be most
understanding. He then explained that he had not
been expecting a great return from the barrows that
had been opened today as they had already attracted
the curiosity of an earlier excavator and any
worthwhile content had been removed. It was
important however to exercise great thoroughness
throughout the entire operation and he would duly
record the events of the day in the absence of Mr
William Cunnington. The Baronet then kindly
extended an invitation for me to visit him in the
library on Monday at noon followed by dinner at five
o' clock to which I gratefully accepted. He then bid
me good evening and as I was departing the Steward
presented me with the five guineas as determined by
Sir Richard and I returned to the Stourhead Inn with
the gold weighing heavily in my pocket.

I have another letter to compose, my Dear Uncle
and it is one that will raise to the fore those mixed and

muddled feelings of this morning and I believe that I shall procrastinate a little longer for I have a thought that requires being committed to the page lest it slips my mind. I shall place myself again on the lofty heights of Whitesheet Hill looking down upon that even plateau witnessing again the steady passage of a ploughman with his team of four. I wonder at that same soil through which the plough has cut year upon year with the toil of the generations throughout all the stages of cultivation. Where are the bones and the burials of these lost centuries of labour? I believe that to study the contents of the barrows of South Wiltshire and to build a history of the ancient peoples from this research is to mislead in the same manner as to take a foreigner on a tour of our grand country houses and estates and inform them that this is how all Englishmen live. Within these barrows are surely the ancient Kings and Queens, Dukes and Baronets and it is to these conspicuous tombs that all antiquaries are inexorably drawn. If I can succeed in but one thing that illuminates the lives of all our ancient ancestors from the Nobleman to the simple ploughman then I should dearly like to present these details to Sir Richard Colt Hoare for he is currently embarking on his great work and it would be as some small repayment for his great generosity towards me. Sir, I shall now bid you goodnight and I shall stir the fire before again taking up my pen and my head clouds over for I know not yet how I shall respond to Mr Robert Foster or how I shall couch my true feelings towards his dear Sister as they must first pass his lips before falling on her ears.

Your obedient servant and Nephew

HENRY CHALK

Fonthill Abbey

Alfred's Tower

Whitesheet Hill

Sunday 18th October 1807

My Dear Uncle,

The resounding bells from Stourhead Church tell me
that it is the Lord's Day and rather than make my way
against the tide of arriving carriages I left the
Stourhead Inn from the rear and followed a steep path
that soon enabled a view back upon that picturesque
vale that is so much the making of the Hoare family,
past and present. On reaching flat ground I thought I
had left the pious behind me yet on a rough path that
crossed fields and hedges I met with a steady
succession of souls that were making their way to a
different church. These were servants and their
families who when questioned informed me that they
were the congregation of nearby Bonham Church. They
were altogether more sombre in their attire and at odds
with the boldness and grandeur of the mustering of the
great and the good in the street outside the church at
Stourton and I believe that the establishment at
Bonham must be a popish chapel. I confess my Dear

Uncle that I did not feel drawn to either establishment but felt content in a quiet contemplation of my own observing the comings and goings of small birds from hedge to hedge and the rustlings and furtive movement of harvest mice. Of all God's creatures it is only our own species that observe a day of worship whilst the remainder go about their business in the hedge, tree or stubble as if days were not labelled with names at all and the warmth of the sun and the distance between dusk and dawn is all. One larger bold and colourful bird caught my eye and impressed me greatly with browns and blues in its make and a stripy black and white bonnet. I observed the progress of this most singular bird from close quarters and compared her to a lady out in her finest clothes until she disgraced herself with a most unholy screeching that did not befit her appearance and a courser tongue in a lady I have yet to experience. In the naming of these creatures I feel largely ignorant but I experience great pleasure in their observation. Near the footpath that conveys the large Catholic population of this village to its place of worship is a field that has been lately cultivated and it has presented me with an opportunity to study the make up of this sandy soil that I believe extends throughout this entire plateau. There are brown stones of hardened sand amongst the sandy soil itself and also in places a peculiar dark and glassy substance that is more dull and coarser than flint and as I now recall the picturesque rock arch that straddles the road near the lake is constructed almost entirely of this material. It has a curious liverish complexion and perhaps has a similar relationship to the sandy rock in the same manner that flint appears wedded to the chalk. As I picked over the ground to my surprise I found a piece of flint glinting darkly in the furrows and I was soon to find many more. I believe that I am not being fanciful my Dear Uncle if I suggest that these exceedingly fresh and well preserved fractures of flint have been caused by the hand of ancient man. In the first instance they are alien to the natural state of the soil here and must therefore have been imported and to confirm my thoughts some have been manipulated to such a high degree and these designs are replicated and are surely no natural accident. I intend to make drawings of some of the finer examples and I feel certain Sir that you will in an instant confirm my own feelings on this matter.

There appears a propensity for long and slender slithers of flint that is of a remarkable quality far exceeding that extracted from the pit on the boundaries of Grovelly Wood by Peter Winter and the edges of these pieces are as sharp as any good razor. The flint occurs here amongst the soil in clusters and as I move away from these concentrations the flint is altogether absent. I recall from observing Peter Winter at his flint work how the waste material lay and accumulated about his feet after a period of time of sitting unmoved in one position and the evidence is comparable here. I can hear your voice asking my Dear Uncle whether this material is not just the detritus from another gunflint industry in the manner of the one that I have described surrounding the pit at Grovelly? I have a conviction Sir that it is not and I shall hopefully convince you in my argument that here is not the source of the flint and this material has been brought from elsewhere and then minutely chipped on this spot to extract the desired pieces. I have already forwarded my drawings of the making of gunflints and you must agree that they bare no comparison in their method. In combination with these slender pieces are also the flint nodules from which they have been struck and on every face of these small fists of black stone are the scars of this gradual reduction. I have also retrieved pieces that bear such remarkable similarities to one another that they must themselves be tools and I can only believe that they are devices for scraping as they each have a distinctly hooked underside and the above surface has then received a great deal of attention and has been rounded to perfection to meet this curved end. Above all I confess that I am perplexed by the freshness of these pieces although there are a minority that have grown cloudy as flint is wont to do and these appear to be the longest and most slender fractures. I am wondering whether it is the nature of the soil in which these pieces have lain that determines their decay or this clouding of the surface for in the main I would gauge that they are much in the condition that they once fell from the makers hand to the earth and from whence I have now retrieved them. It is a great conundrum Sir as to the period of time between these two events.

I then walked across this level plain of sandy soil, to the foot of the chalk lands where Whitesheet Hill and its ancient earth works and burial mounds are in constant view and I made my return passing as I did the Red Lion Inn which stands on the crossroads of the London Road. I found in turn, where areas of cultivated land permitted my inspection, a uniformity in the nature of this brown sandy soil and indeed further evidence of these small clusters of fashioned flint. I could not collect all that I encountered but instead made a plan showing their position and I have now, as I write these words, emptied my pockets of all their sand covered content and I shall make a proper inspection. I intend to spend the rest of the evening making studies of these flint pieces which I shall then present to Sir Richard in his library at noon tomorrow.

No sooner had I embarked on the exercise of inspection and illustration when I heard a familiar and welcome voice outside on the landing and "Boots" made a knocking upon my door and announced that I had visitor. I was very pleased to receive Mr Richard Fenton and I apologised for the disarray in my quarters as I had every possible surface covered with unfinished correspondence and broken flint. Mr Fenton made light of this issue and I invited him to settle before the coal blaze and I called for a brandy to make as warm a welcome as I was able. Mr Fenton then apologised for his intrusion at this late hour but wished to confirm that I was in no way ailing as my presence had been anticipated at Stourhead Church this morning and it was thought that there must be some malign reason for my absence. There then followed the most awkward of situations which still hangs in the air and it is entirely of my own making. At Mr Fenton's initial enquiry I felt myself redden visibly for I could not readily explain my absence at the morning service and I was indeed lost for words. My guest then clasped his hand to his mouth in a realisation that perhaps I had attended a church after all, but that it was one of an opposing faith " I . . . I . . . I you are a C . . . C . . . Cath . . . ? How most dreadfully impertinent of me . . . I . . . I . . . understand completely…We had no . . . idea . . . " Mr Fenton then took a large tip of his brandy glass to rectify his composure whilst I was in a great state of anxiety not knowing which was considered the greater sin; to be of the Catholic faith or to abstain from a church service of any denomination and instead to wander about the fields all the day with my hands in the soil. My Dear Uncle I confess that I then said nothing which I acknowledge is a poor tactic that I often employ in these the most awkward of situations. This silence appeared to suit Mr Fenton as he was quickly able to change the subject of conversation and fill the void with the first matter which entered his head as he looked about the room. "So you collect stones Mr Chalk? Then you will have much to discuss with Mr William Cunnington when you next meet for he is a great collector of the same and you are a writer of copious letters also?" I informed Mr Fenton that I had been recording the events of my pedestrian excursion in a series of letters and that I had made use of more writing paper, bent more nibs and drained more bottles of ink that I thought possible. To this information Mr Fenton clapped his hands together with a crack and even rose from his chair in his display of enthusiasm. "You are a man after my own heart Sir" and he then demanded my hand so that he might shake it vigorously before continuing his enquiry. "And this correspondence, what is to become of it? Is the recipient to publish and what has been your agreement?" I confessed that there had been no agreement and I knew not what was to become of my letters. On hearing this news my guest then folded back into the chair and clasped his hand to his chin and then remained in that fixed position so that I dared not interrupt this reverie. Finally and with a sudden movement that made me start he demanded a pen and paper to which on taking receipt of he then thrust back into my hands as he again leapt to his feet and paced backwards and forwards on the hearth before the blazing fire. I knew not what task it was that I was set to record as I waited with my pen poised above the page. "A tour . . . " My guest gestured that I should commence in my written duty and he then ceased his circuit of the hearth to question why I had chosen to make my pedestrian tour here in Wiltshire and not in Gloucestershire, Devonshire or his own county of Pembrokeshire? I believe my answer was a cause of some surprise for he repeated it over and again "Chalk . . . Chalk . . . Chalk?" I explained briefly about my observations during the digging of the great well in the brewery yard at Southall which seemed to satisfy my inquisitor. "I see, chalk it is then" and he then returned to his original purpose; " A tour, in search of chalk, through parts of South Wiltshire, in the year

1807, written in a series of letters to . . . to whom are you corresponding Sir?" I then informed Mr Fenton that it was to you, my Dear Uncle that I had been directing the entire account of my experiences. "To an uncle. Is he lost? . . . Lost is best, it lends to more drama, . . . to a lost uncle . . . encountering on the way . . . let me see . . . a Charcoal Burner, together with a visit to Stonehenge, Fonthill Abbey . . . it may be a false trail but it will sell . . . and Stourhead, interspersed with various anecdotes and, I will wager Mr Chalk some antiquarian observations, am I not correct? . . . and to conclude . . . it must be anonymous which is of course a false modesty as not only is the author's true identity woven into the title page it will also be liberally sprinkled about between the covers of the book and it will gratify the reader in making him elucidate the ownership of the piece. So by . . . by . . . whom? Why by A. Pedestrian of course. There must be every kind of typeface and bold lettering employed in this title page and it should be rushed to meet the printers deadline and on the book stands before the year is out. There, is that not sufficient?" Mr Fenton then returned to his chair and drained his brandy with an expression of great satisfaction and I believe that he is at his happiest when he can explore a humorous avenue until he can reasonably go no further. On the inspection of my written account of his presentation he shook his head and made utterances before taking up the pen himself to make a better order of my work. My guest now assumed an air of great expectation and I now began to realise that he was indeed sincere in his proposals regarding the publication of my letters. I confessed that this never was my intention to which he appeared greatly disappointed and was at a loss to understand my apprehension "Sir I can assure you that it is the only course, you travel, you correspond, you embellish and then you publish, the printing presses in Paternoster Row are a blur of ink and machinery and the bookstands in the Capital are creaking under the very weight of such publications. I confess I know not where lies the problem." I called for another brandy for my guest to rescue him from this glumness and you can be certain that Mr Fenton will not remain downcast for any period of time for his character simply will not I believe permit such behaviour and in no time an air of conviviality had returned to the room. Mr Fenton then

asked after you my Dear Uncle for as the recipient of
my correspondence you had featured in his design for
the title page of the proposed publication of my
scribbles but you may rest assured Sir it is but one of
Mr Fenton's more fanciful notions for who would wish
to read of the thoughts and deeds of one so immature. I
was able to give an account of my childhood memories
when you then lived in the Metropolis and your
occasional visits to our family home and I can recall
your patience in lining up my soldiers only for me to
then carelessly destroy these opposing toy armies. I am
saddened that distance, these last ten years, has
dictated that we should only make our written
communications and I believe that my Father, your
Brother, showed little encouragement whenever I made
a request that we should again meet in person for I
believe that you will find me almost beyond recognition
from that small boy that you once knew. I sincerely
hope my Dear Uncle that there is now no obstacle to the
arranging of this event that we can again be reunited. I
was able to relate to Mr Fenton the details of your own
pedestrian adventure in North Wales and he informed
me that it was a part of the world that inspired awe in

all who had the good fortune to visit that wild and wonderful and most secretive of places. Indeed our very discussion has resulted in an invitation from Mr Fenton to act as my guide in a future excursion to that same place which excites me greatly. My hand trembles before the page as during my discussion with Mr Fenton he then asked after your business as I gauge that he found himself in accord with your adventurous spirit and wished to know more of you. I confess that I know not of your business but I recall in a conversation that perhaps was not intended for my ears between my Father and a bank official that you had encountered some financial misfortune which then resulted in your move from London to a place called Fleet. My Father would never elucidate when asked about the whereabouts of this town or perhaps even a village by this name and he commanded me to talk no more about it. At the mention of this place called Fleet Mr Fenton at once drew a grave expression and leant forward to clasp my hands in his and by this display of consternation I knew it not be a good place at all. My Dear Uncle why have you not approached your own family, my Father when he was alive, with a request for help rather than face the incarceration of a debtors prison? I knew not that such places existed and I cannot imagine the horror and desperation that you must have endured. I would dearly like to put right that wrong that our family has caused and yet I cannot anticipate my own position as I have turned my own back on the future that my Father had determined for me. I sincerely hope that your own position is now more secure and I am now ashamed at the great display of indulgence with the daily succession of my trivial correspondence that is of no consequence. Mr Fenton was distressed that he should be the one to make this dreadful situation known to me but he has assured me that sadly it is a common enough event in business and a full recovery is often accomplished. Mr Fenton has asked me to forward his fondest regards and he is of the firm belief that your situation is now secure. As a former Lawyer Mr Fenton states that he is able to make such an assertion on the evidence that one who is without good resource would not embark upon and then publish an account of their own pedestrian tour as it speaks loudly of financial security and it is also an action that is to be commended and one that his nephew must surely have the good sense to follow.

I cannot stress enough the friendship I have found in Mr Fenton for although I felt great alarm to learn of your past circumstances I believe in my friend's assertions that you have now made fully your recovery and I sincerely hope that this description of my conversation with Mr Fenton has not embarrassed in any way or awoken past memories that you must wish to forget. It has brought me closer still with my feelings towards you my Dear Uncle and confirmed my commitment that we should soon be reunited.

It is not the evening that I had planned upon yet it has given me much to think about and my sandy stones have been neglected until another time for with Mr Fenton's departure and my completion of this letter to you, I am now more than ready for slumber.

Your obedient and faithful Nephew,
HENRY CHALK

Monday 19th October 1807

M Y D E A R U N C L E ,

Today I find myself in very noble surrounds as Sir
Richard Colt Hoare has kindly admitted me to his
great library and here I sit before a beautifully crafted
desk where I now commit these lines to you. I believe
that the Baronet is suffering from an illness called
gout and is in some considerable pain as he has now
retired for the afternoon. I feel that I am writing in a
whisper such is the effect of this place with its great
looming tiers of leather bound erudition crushing my
very small notions that I have formed of late. I felt
myself redden at the collar when being addressed by
Sir Richard as he kindly explained the great project
he has embarked upon that is to be called "The
Ancient History of Wiltshire". There are maps of
tracts of the south of this county drawn up by a
gentleman called Mr Philip Crocker who is the
surveyor and draughtsman appointed to this task. The
content of each barrow has its own illustration and

there is a great beauty to both the maps and the plates of drawings. Indeed the organisation of this grand project is profound with Mr William Cunnington as co-adjutator with a responsibility for the opening of the barrows with the two barrow diggers themselves, Mr Steven Parker and Mr John Parker, Mr Philip Crocker the surveyor and draughtsman and Sir Richard himself the Commander and author who will commit to the page the facts and conclusions of this great exercise. I do not fully understand the role of Mr Richard Fenton in these proceedings except that he is perhaps an aide to the Baronet and there is surely a friend no more committed than is Mr Fenton to his noble host. Mr Fenton brings warmth to the place for he cannot resist a humorous view even in the most solemn of moments and as I have discovered today Sir Richard alone is not one to encourage dialogue but then I flatter myself that I have something to offer to such a well planned enquiry. I have a pocket full of flints and a head full of notions and I wished that I could again meet with Mr William Cunnington as I consider that he is a man who believes in what the eye can perceive rather than what is already written on the page. My Dear Uncle, if you were within reach of my ear I feel certain that you would box it and speak to me very firmly with a reminder that I am sitting in the best private library in the land and I should put down my pen and for once suspend my flow of nonsense.

Sir, I may have contrived your words and deeds but it was surely the very best of advice for which I am truly thankful. After a circuit of this room I knew not where to start with numismatics, the writings of Tacitus, Caesar and Pliny and the topographies of every possible county. I instead settled upon books already selected and laying open and available on Sir Richard's desk and one volume displayed plates of Stonehenge and a short article by Mr William Maton relating to the fall of one of the major sets of stones in 1797. I thought back to my recent visit to that place and the description of this same ground shaking event by the toothless shepherd who was swift to approach our windswept party and engage our sympathy. The illustrations depict a before and after view of the effects of this fall and in both were present the same Lady and Gentleman, an artistic device to suggest the scale of the structure to the viewer, but by their very persistent presence and air of affected innocence I fancied that they must in some way be culpable. I turned the pages of this same volume and my heart took a great leap as before me were two plates that appeared to be illustrations of a similar flint object that I had collected from outside the brickearth pit in Salisbury and the circumstances for the provenance of these crafted flint pieces were identical in every way. The author of this short account is Mr John Frere and the location of this find is Hoxne in the county of Suffolk in the year of 1797. Mr Frere describes these objects as "Flint weapons" and that they lay in great numbers at a depth of twelve feet amongst the strata of a brickearth pit and in combination were found "Some extraordinary bones, particularly a jaw bone of enormous size, of some unknown animal, with the teeth remaining in it." On receiving this information I fell back into Sir Richard Colt Hoare's chair that was placed before his desk with these words encircling my head. I asked out loud to a library empty of souls save my own, "Why and how can this information lie dormant and not be considered a matter of extreme import and astonishment?" I have not heard The Baronet or Mr William Cunnington make any reference to this discovery that happened barely ten years before. It is as if Mr Frere has been alone in his comprehension despite his reporting of these events to the Society of Antiquaries and their subsequent publication in this edition of their Proceedings which was issued in 1800. I gathered up my senses and completed my reading of this article and I submit this lengthy tract in Mr Frere's own words as it only confirms my own thoughts, ideas and indeed strong instinct that has been haunting my mind and dreams since the first day of my pedestrian excursion here in this County;

"The situation in which these weapons were found may tempt us to refer them to a very remote period indeed; even beyond that of the present world; but, whatever our conjectures on that head may be, it will be difficult to account for the stratum in which they lie being covered with another stratum, which, on that supposition, may be conjectured to have been once the bottom, or at least the shore, of the sea. The manner in which they lie would lead to the persuasion that it was a place of their manufacture and not of their accidental deposit; and the numbers of them were so great that the man who carried on the brick-work told me that, before he was aware of their being objects of curiosity, he had emptied baskets full of them into the ruts of the adjoining road."

My Dear Uncle the earlier account of the twisting of my own ankle in the ruts in the road outside the Salisbury brickworks will tell you that the circumstances are identical in this respect and indeed in all respects to that of Hoxne in Suffolk. Mr John Frere's words have fully reinforced my own belief that the dark period of our ancient ancestors extends to a time when the land was not yet truly formed as we know it today and yet behind this veil of ignorance we now have a beacon of light. Is it not the common substance that we call flint that is the key to the continuity of life itself upon this earth and is not the instance of the very first discovery as to its remarkable fire giving properties and keenness of edge that has sent Man on his remarkable journey? The flint fragments that litter the sandy fields beneath Whitesheet Hill are I believe the detritus of more modern and settled farming societies and I do not mock when I refer to man as "Modern" before even the advent of the use of metal. Sir I apologise for I am dealing in incomprehensible fact and would be branded a man not in his right senses if I were to broadcast this view beyond these pages. I would welcome an audience with Mr John Frere as I believe his frustration must be as great as any man for his printed word collects dust and is ignored by those who do not understand the importance of such a discovery. I must now depart to my lodgings to then return for dinner at five o clock at Stourhead House although I now draw strength from the knowledge that my burden is not imaginary nor is it solitary.

My Dear Uncle I have now acquired a compulsion to write even at this late hour for it was almost midnight when I returned from Stourhead House but I feel alive and some distance from making acquaintance again with my pillow. I trust that you can imagine the grandeur of dining with Sir Richard Colt Hoare and his selected guests. Dinner is at the respectable hour of five o clock and I ensured that I at least had a clean white shirt for the occasion. It is not clean now and I shall reveal in time how this occurred and you will, Sir, not be surprised to learn that Mr John Fenton has a part to play in that tale. The guests were few in number and of those whom I had not yet met were a young lawyer by the name of Mr Edward Phelps and another young man of fashion who had earlier arrived from London by the name of Mr George Button who was more than familiar with Mr John Fenton. Mr Philip Crocker who is the surveyor and draughtsman to the Baronet was also present and I wished for an opportunity to remark on the great skill involved in his illustrations and plans for "Ancient Wiltshire". Mr Crocker was seated across at an opposing end of the great table to myself and then retired early to prepare for an excursion in the morning and so that I was unable to make my compliment. There were no ladies present which permitted an air of relaxed familiarity with much humour and laughter. Mr Richard Fenton was, I am glad to be able to report, sitting directly across the table from my position which was a detail that offered me great reassurance. It was this same Gentleman that proposed the first toast of the evening in an

acknowledgement of the privilege of dining in such a
superior room " . . . and although our number may be
few we recognise the great honour that our host has
bestowed upon us this evening and I propose a toast
of thanks to our noble host Sir Richard Colt Hoare."
A sympathy to which we all heartily concurred and we
then raised our glasses in unison. Indeed the Saloon
is as grand a surroundings as I ever imagined and is
quite the distraction for the partaking of food as I
gauge that it is fully fifty feet in length with the
ceiling rich in its ornamentation and with large
painted panels on each wall and the whole is
furnished throughout with style and magnificence.
Before me on the table lay an array of silver cutlery
that I approached with great caution and I sincerely
hope that I did not broadcast my attempted discretion
as I followed the example of the other guests as they
greeted each of the many courses. As I negotiated my
way through the earlier passage of dinner, in amongst
such a display of social confidence, I felt increasingly
that my presence here was a gross error. What did I
know about events in the channel or of the siege of
Copenhagen although I dutifully raised my glass? Mr

Richard Fenton, perhaps sensing my discomfort, then drew attention to my presence and demanded that a toast was drunk to "Mr Henry Chalk, our pedestrian tourist and adventurer" and I felt my self redden as I am so often wont to do in any such situation. The company were most warm and generous in making this toast and Mr Richard Fenton then flattered me greatly by his suggestion that I was an "Antiquary in the making" at which point more wine was imbibed and I felt helpless to resist. The young gentleman of fashion, Mr Button, then proclaimed that there was already plenty enough of that species who were only too ready to make acquaintance with the dust of their ancestors and "..surely young Mr Chalk was not to be encouraged". Mr Button then proposed that I should be directed to more useful and becoming pursuits after all it is well known that "what antiquaries do not know they make up anyway". Being seated at the table of Sir Richard Colt Hoare the man of fashion was soon shouted down and his comments that I can now comfortably identify as raillery were all taken in good humour. Mr Richard Fenton then rose to his feet and speaking in those rich theatrical tones, to which I

have now become accustomed, he made a firm
rebuttal to this onslaught; "We speak from facts not
theory and it is our duty as fellow antiquarians to cast
aside the shrouds of darkness and mystery and reveal
to all the history and lives of these ancient inhabitors
of our land for we must not forget that they were real
people like ourselves. Our fashionable friend would
have us believe that the sole purpose and industry of
our ancestors was to cast artefacts and broken urns
across the green sward that is Salisbury Plain to keep
us in employ and far from mischief in their reverential
and not inexpensive recovery." These words induced
cheers and support from around the table and Mr
Richard Fenton appeared well satisfied with his stout
defence of the antiquarian battlements yet I felt that
the comedy of his delivery had disguised the gravity
of his observation. I found myself bolstered by the
flowing wine and I brought my hand down on the table
and startled the host and guests alike as I discharged
a piece of cutlery from the table to the floor. Having
now attracted the attention of the entire company I
felt that I must continue with my support for Mr
Richard Fenton; "Sir, you have put into words my own

feelings and thoughts and as always with great wit and eloquence that I cannot hope to emulate. It is indeed the relics of our ancestors that are retrieved by the persevering antiquary and I concur wholeheartedly with Mr Fenton that they once belonged to real people." I bent down to retrieve the knife from the carpet before the footman could round the table and undertake the task and I then held it aloft. "Gentlemen, this is a knife but I would not be buried with it today" to which Mr John Fenton remarked; "It is one of a set Sir and it would not do for it would then make it an odd set." Amidst more laughter I continued on my course to I knew not where; "It is but a tool and our ancient ancestors, before a time of metal, would have knives also for how else would they cut up their meat as we are cutting up ours this evening? I suggest that every man had his knife and not just the kings, queens and warriors that have now had their slumber disturbed. I propose that these common tools were fashioned from the flint that abounds in the south of this county and these discarded tools still lay about the fields where they once fell all those generations ago. Indeed I have

examples about my person.." At this point Sir
Richard Colt Hoare slowly rose from his chair and
with a pained expression excused himself from the
table and naturally we the present company pushed
back our chairs and rose as one as the Baronet then
left the room. There was a great deal of sympathy
expressed for the obvious suffering of our host and
once the diners were reunited with their chairs then
the subject took a different course and I believed that
my observations on the widespread use of flint tools
had been lost amongst the fields of idle conservation.
In due course Mr Philip Crocker excused himself to
attend to his work and Mr Richard Fenton then
declared that he had duties to perform and in turn
excused himself also. I was for returning to my
accommodation as a hand of cards was suggested to
which I felt no inclination. I warmed myself at the
great fireplace before departing and I was looking up
at the chimney piece carved from the finest white
marble as Mr John Fenton approached. He then
retrieved the subject of my observation that I thought
had fallen upon deaf ears and suggested that if
antiquarians were to be taken seriously then they

should be able to prove their theories. I then declared that I had the evidence on my person and I first produced my flint tool from the Salisbury brickearth pit and stated that I had intended to show it to Sir Richard earlier today in combination with a number of pieces fashioned by human hand. I explained its provenance and it was then passed to Mr Phelps and even the man of fashion, Mr Button, tested its edge. I then displayed the tool that had recently been manufactured by Peter Winter and this was also passed between the remaining company and its freshly prepared edge was acknowledged as being keen and sharp to the touch. Mr John Fenton then suggested that he had a notion of how my theory could be put to the test which must surely be the correct course if we are a breed to be taken seriously and he then indicated that we should all follow after him. We were taken to an outbuilding across the courtyard where the game larder was situated, the night was cold and our breath made great clouds in the lamplight. We were presented with the sight of various species of bird and game all dangling from hooks with their shadows wavering in false animation on the back wall. I gathered that some form of demonstration was required to back up my words and suggested that a large rabbit, that Mr Fenton informed me was called a "hare", would suffice for our purposes but Mr Fenton stated that if we were going to take this matter seriously then it demanded a larger beast and he proposed that it must be a deer. "There is your meat Mr Henry Chalk and you are now the ancestor of all butchers." As you will be aware my Dear Uncle I had observed the clandestine butchery of a deer in the stable of the New Inn some days ago and I had now drunk sufficient wine to believe that I could replicate this task in the name of science. I am not sickened by the sight of such things and agreed to prove my case but I required help lowering the beast onto the large wooden chopping board and for the light to then be positioned in my favour. The carcass had been previously cleaned with the head and lower limbs removed. I then parted with my coat and rolled up my sleeves and chose the tool replicated by Peter Winter as it presented the sharpest edge. I recalled how I had observed its maker when he had turned it about in his hand and found favour with holding it between thumb and forefinger and at the first incision the man of fashion produced a handkerchief from his pocket and buried his long nose in it exclaiming his disgust at the sight and smell of the operation. Mr John Fenton returned to the house for wine to assist with the viewing and returned also with another lamp. I experimented with my crude butchery skills and favoured tugging at the skin with my free hand and making it taut and then presenting it to the cutting edge. I could then roll the tool between thumb and forefinger along this tightness which would in turn easily part the skin from the flesh. I found a cloth to clear the collected fat from the flint and fully forgot my audience as I made good progress. I employed the same method to the jointing of the meat but found difficulty in dealing with the bone itself but I had successfully removed several parcels of the meat and was now attacking the haunches. It was at this moment that the young lawyer, Mr Phelps, made a suggestion that shocked me greatly;"Was this not the beast that Sir Richard himself shot last week and was intended as a gift for Mr Matthew Fortesque and was to be transported in the morning to London?" Mr

Fenton then feigned surprise and said "I do believe
that you are correct Mr Phelps" Mr Button then
concluded from behind his handkerchief "By the time
young Mr Chalk has finished with it I think only fit for
a peasant stew". I was aghast as the three young men
then burst out into uncontrollable laughter and taking
one lamp with them they then withdrew from the game
larder bidding me a "Good night master butcher,
perhaps your stone wedge can be put to good use to
prop open the door when you leave". I have been made
a fool of by Mr John Fenton whose appetite for such
things is I fear insatiable and I believed them sincere
in their interest. At first the tears streamed down my
cheeks as I thought of my betrayal of the kind Baronet's
hospitality and I could not comprehend the purpose of
Mr John Fenton's cruel humour any more than I could
excuse my own foolishness. As best I could I
completed my task and stacked up the crude joints on
the wooden board with the skin, bones and remnants to
one side. I found a pump and bucket in the yard and
drew water to wash the mess from my hands as I heard
the clock strike one quarter to midnight. I did not wish
to reach the Inn after midnight as I would be required

to raise the staff and make an inconvenience and so I determined to make good time back to the Stourhead Inn. I found my way around the side of the house and then extinguishing the lantern I left it in a small porch that must be the access to the domestic quarters. The night was clear enough to see before me the broad drive with the dark and grotesque shapes of the twisted chestnut trees and I felt a shiver pass over me as if I were again a young child who feared the unknown terrors of the night. I began to walk and then run faster and in turn faster still until I could feel the cold night air forcing into my face and I believed that I could keep abreast with the fastest racehorse. My ankle felt strong and I know that all the paths on the Baronet's estate are kept in the best order possible and as my feet pounded I felt no fear of stumbling and falling. I could sense the stone gateway looming ahead of me and I slowed my pace least the gatekeeper should be startled by a person fleeing through the night but once I met the road I again flew down the hill through the darkness to the Stourhead Inn with my footfalls resounding between the steep embankments on either side. I slipped quietly through the back door and once inside my room I soon heard the clock strike midnight.

I do not know how I shall explain myself to Sir Richard Colt Hoare yet I feel in some way justified in my actions for I did fulfil the challenge that those disingenuous young men had concocted for me. I consider that they mock me for my too serious nature in one so young for I do not truly believe that Mr John Fenton dislikes me but I care the less for what people think of me and I will follow my own trail. There is one for whom I care greatly and I hope with all my heart that this feeling is reciprocated. Even at this late hour I must send a note to Miss Foster's Brother to ensure that he should suspend any further correspondence to myself at the Stourhead Inn. Tomorrow, my Dear Uncle, I shall leave this place and again become a simple pedestrian tourist for my ankle is now fully repaired and I shall make a resolution to not be drawn so readily into the lives of all whom I meet for it seems only to lead to complication.

Your serious yet still foolish Nephew,
HENRY CHALK

Tuesday 20th October 1807

M Y D E A R U N C L E ,

Sir it is my grave responsibility to report that tragedy
has struck and under the most unfortunate
circumstances for which I can only attach the blame
to myself and my own selfish and foolish actions. I
believe that it is best to recount the events of the
morning in the order that they occurred and yet I fear
my Dear and Faithful Uncle that in whichever
arrangement these facts are presented they will cause
you great distress. At breakfast I was approached by
the Landlord and informed that the Parish Constable
wished to interview me, an event for which I quickly
prepared myself and descended to the front of the
building as instructed. At first I believed that the
butchery of the deer had in some manner been drawn
to the attention of the parish official yet I was soon to
discover that there was a far more serious purpose to
his enquiry. I was led to an outhouse by the Landlord
and the Parish Constable where on a large rough table

the body of a man was laid out and I felt that their eyes were upon me as I was presented with this tragic sight. I could not at first place where I had seen this unfortunate Gentleman but I felt the stirrings of some recognition and the Parish Constable was made to repeat his initial question as his words became lost to me as if I were embattled in some malevolent dream. "Mr Chalk? You arrived late back at the Inn did you not Sir?" I explained that I had indeed returned just before midnight. The Parish Constable revealed that the deceased had been found lying in the middle of the road by a milkmaid early this morning at a point halfway between the Stourhead Inn and the stone gateway to the house. I informed them that the lane was dark and overhung with trees and I felt certain that I would have stumbled upon the body had it been there when I passed that way for I surely would not have seen it. I now believed that I was under some suspicion for the enquiry then turned to the bloody gash on the forehead of the dead man and in turn to my white shirt of yesterday that I had earlier submitted to the maid for washing but was now produced before me and I was asked to explain its condition. I assured the two gentlemen that the now dried dark brown bloodstains were most certainly animal and not human and it was a circumstance that would be difficult to explain here but could easily be proven if required. The Parish Constable, then produced a folded letter from his coat pocket and with the same grim and unaltered expression requested that I should read it and then explain its content. It was addressed to a Mr Joseph Barklay of Exeter with a request that he should; "Advance to Hindon at once and put up at the Lamb Inn until I can establish the movement of our subject Mr Henry Chalk." The note was dated 12th of October and signed "J Chalk". I had no sooner digested the content of one short letter when I was presented with another which also displayed your signature my Dear Uncle and had been posted on 15th October; "Our subject will be staying at the Stourhead Inn. Put up at the Red Lion Inn, Kilmington. Ask no questions and do not draw the attention of anyone. Once you have delivered your message return to Exeter and I shall honour the second instalment of your fee". The Parish official then held up further property that had been retrieved from Mr Joseph Barklay for it was

discovered that on his person was a cloth purse
containing a little short of ten guineas. I must have
appeared in a state of weakness for the Landlord
guided me to a place where I could sit as the true
meaning of all these events now formed in my mind.
My gaze was drawn to the profile of the dead man, his
staring but unseeing eyes and the grey lifelessness of
his skin and no more would his broad chest rise and
fall with the drawing of breath. I recalled aloud the
circumstances that had proceeded this fateful
situation, the details of which you are only too painfully
aware my Dear Uncle, and I informed them also of my
regular correspondence to you containing my deeds
and whereabouts that had alerted you to my
predicament and prompted the execution of your plan
to come to my aid. From my seated position on an old
beer barrel I then stood before the table and studied the
visage of the corpse in more detail and I then realised
where I had before seen Mr Joseph Barklay and I felt a
sudden chill at this recollection. It was on the occasion
of my visit to the village of Hindon when by the light of
a chestnut brazier I had felt his unsettling gaze upon
me and he had also pursued me for a little way. I

thought him then to be a man in Mr William Beckfords'
employ and feared the attention that he had paid me
but I now realise Sir that he was engaged to execute
your own plan. I informed the Gentlemen of this fact
and lamented deeply that if only I had let him approach
me on that Election night he would have carried out his
duty and returned to his family in Exeter some days
ago. The Parish Constable thanked me earnestly for my
cooperation in elucidating the necessary facts and that
he was sorry for the obvious discomfort that his enquiry
had caused me. I was informed that by good fortune
there was a guest staying at the Inn who was a Doctor of
Medicine by profession and he had agreed to give a
cursory examination of the body in due course. I then
returned to my room and sat for an age in a blank daze
not knowing what course to take. It is plain My Dear
Uncle that my foolish exploits have cost the life of your
poor associate for knowing my state of impecuniosity
you dispatched a letter immediately to Mr Joseph
Barklay for him to then come to my aid and whilst he
awaited instruction at Hindon by chance he observed
a young pedestrian tourist who then unfortunately
eluded him. In time you received the further accounts

of my progress which you then relayed to the long suffering Mr Barklay and so he was able to locate me at Stourhead and there he remained faithful to your instructions by behaving with the utmost discretion. Rather than make a direct approach to my place of lodging he waited to intercept me perhaps at a far later hour than he first imagined but he remained the model of patience in executing his duty.

The Parish Official has again sought me out and I have been informed that the Medical man has viewed the body of Mr Barklay and he is of the opinion that the unfortunate man died of a heart seizure and the blow to the head was consistent with the subsequent fall to the ground on his collapse. As I flew through the night at that late hour from Stourhead House I unknowingly passed your associate who was perhaps ailing then for he surely could not have caught up with me and common sense suggests that he would have called out my name had he been able. An open knife has also been found on the road that must have fallen from the pocket of the late Mr Barklay and the Parish Constable considers that it provided him with the protection necessary when burdened with the task of carrying a purse containing that not inconsiderable sum. The Official then instructed me that Mr William Whitmarsh the Coroner has been summoned from Salisbury for it is his official duty to preside over and register the cause of all deaths in his District before any burial can take place. He then shook his head and said that it was indeed a sorry end to a plan that had been undertaken with the very best of intentions and I informed him that I would contact you at once to report these dreadful events. I found the Parish Constable to be a stern but also a learned and kindly man and altogether a different type of Gentleman from his equal that I encountered some days ago at the "New Inn" who appeared devoid of all manners and any semblance of integrity. The Steward at Stourhead house is to be informed of these tragic events and is then to be entrusted with the body of Mr Joseph Barklay and his property until the arrival of the Coroner in due course.

I have another onerous duty to perform for I must now write to Sir Richard Colt Hoare to humbly apologise for destroying the deer carcass that he intended as a gift to a Gentleman in London. I hold my head in my hands when I consider the trouble I have caused at my every turn. For what it is worth I shall endeavour to explain my misguided action which I undertook in the name of a practical scientific experiment but I feel certain that it will not meet with his approval. I shall also include my thoughts on the everyday use of flint by ancient man in the Baronet's own neighbourhood of Stourton. I have a conviction of their correctness and I shall accompany this description with the drawings of the flint pieces that I have undertaken thus far. I will submit also an illustration of the flint tool from the Salisbury brickearth pit and a sketch of the overlying strata with a reference to the printed account of Mr John Frere and his most remarkable discovery in Hoxne in Suffolk that resides in the pages of a book within the Baronet's own library. Sir Richard Colt Hoare has far exceeded the bounds of common generosity towards this troublesome pedestrian tourist and I fear that he will not accept a financial settlement of the debt that I feel that I have incurred as a result of his hospitality. The author of The History of Ancient Wiltshire can assess the small worth of my own contribution and do with it what he will as he shapes his own account of this dark and remote period.

I know not what else to relate my Dear Uncle and I dispatch this final correspondence to you with the heaviest of hearts. When I am able I fully intend to reimburse you for the expense that you have incurred on my behalf and I shall do likewise to the family of the late Mr Joseph Barklay.

Before sealing this letter to you my Dear Uncle I have been visited by my good friend Mr Richard Fenton. He has been informed of the sudden death of your associate by the Steward at Stourhead House and wished to convey his own sympathies and those of our host Sir Richard Colt Hoare who has also now learned of this tragedy. Both Gentlemen have expressed their desire to commend you on your own actions in attempting to come to my aid, knowing as you did my precarious situation. Mr Fenton has informed me that once the Coroner has carried out his official duty, then the Baronet will arrange and make provision for the burial of poor Mr Barklay.

My visitor then remarked on the incident of the previous night for he had overheard Mr Button making laughter at breakfast and naturally enquired as to its cause. There appeared a reticence between

the three young men present to divulge any
information until Mr Richard Fenton insisted that his
son Mr John Fenton should explain this behaviour.
The account of the visit to the game larder was then
related and as with the occasion of the wager that was
struck between Mr John Fenton and myself at the
George Inn in Amesbury an excess of wine and high
spirits was given as its cause. Mr Richard Fenton
then asked whether I should ever get used to his sons
propensity for raillery and mischief making and he
cautioned me to never entertain any idea or proposal
from that same gentleman for there will surely only
ever be one outcome. I asked what was to become of
the intended gift from Sir Richard to the Gentleman
in London and I was assured that the matter had been
swiftly dealt with and no harm has been done. The
Baronet has been informed that the carcass was
already maggot blown and he will be required to again
pick up his gun which is a pursuit that will only result
in pleasure and the encounter with fresh air will serve
to raise his spirits. Mr Fenton then asked of my future
plans and I explained that the tragedy here had made
me reflect deeply on the consequences of my actions

and the effect of those actions upon others. I informed him that I fully intended to depart for London in the morning to fulfil my Father's wishes and accept my family responsibility. Mr Fenton then surprised me greatly by speaking with great sincerity about love and I shall try to recall his every word as they touched me greatly. "You will have noticed a sadness in Sir Richard's eye and it is a melancholy that has been with him since before I was fortunate enough to make his acquaintance, indeed you can detect it in the portrait of Father and Son in the reception hall. It is not a matter that he will speak of even to his closest friends and I am indeed flattered to class myself as such. In 1785 Sir Richard lost his beloved wife in childbirth. He was heartbroken then and he is heartbroken now as the heart is the most difficult of devices to mend but he lives and he smiles and sometimes he will laugh. Above all our noble friend needs distraction which he seeks in the task of recording the antiquities of Wiltshire and it is indeed a very worthy cause but it will never replace the loss he has suffered. A coldness has settled on his heart which can affect how you treat even your own family.

One day he will be reunited with his beloved Hestor and only when his heart ceases to beat will it also cease to ache. You are young but you will learn that love can be a force of great power and its loss can defeat the greatest and strongest of men and if you find love Mr Henry Chalk you may forever regret the losing of that love. Young men sometimes think that they love when all is confusion and some speak of love knowing that it is a powerful word that can unlock the heart and passion of a woman but love is more than words uttered at an opportune moment."

I do not know why Mr Fenton chose to tell me of Sir Richard's most intimate of circumstances or how he thought that it would affect my situation yet after his departure from my room I sat with these words resounding in my head. I believe that my good friend has spoken in a very wise and paternal way to help guide my decisions as he must sense that my ramble here is a diversion from my duties elsewhere and indeed he is correct. I have reflected now about my own Father, your Brother, and how he may also have suffered a broken heart at the death of my Mother for I was too young to understand his pain but I grew up knowing his coldness and perhaps a heart can become so cold that it is no longer capable of warmth. Love must be a fundamental thing that binds people as one and to lose love is to become cast adrift alone on a cold sea.

I cannot now forward my letter to Sir Richard Colt Hoare as he is not aware of the incident with the deer to which I allude and then apologise for whole-heartedly. I feel that these matters are only mere distractions and I flatter myself greatly that I can help to contribute to his pioneering work. I have therefore posted the letter into the fire place where it meets with the conflagrations of the Radstock coal and with it perish my own foolish antiquarian aspirations.

Mr Richard Fenton I sincerely hope that I shall meet again for his wisdom has guided me towards a reconciliation where I feel I should now embrace my Father's wishes. I believe that he has been able to look into my very soul and as I write these words I can also hear his mellifluous voice ". . . if you find love Mr Henry Chalk you may forever regret the losing of that love"

Sir, you will be glad to learn that my stock of writing paper is now exhausted, my nibs blunt and my ink well dry. I shall give the callous on my finger a much required rest as I believe that I have initiated and then documented quite enough disruption in the south of this quiet county of Wiltshire and I feel certain that the population here shall be glad to witness my departure.

On my adventure I have now met with a division in the path ahead and Mr John Cary cannot on this occasion assist for neither destination on this handpost are recorded on his plan. Indeed there exists no map that can offer this confused and love tormented traveller the guidance he requires for despite the best of advice he knows not whether he should now follow his head or his heart. Bless you my dear Uncle for if the former shall be my guide then you will know where to locate your troublesome relation yet if I should choose "the peaks and troughs of adventure", I know not what fate awaits this pedestrian tourist.

I am forever your faithful Nephew,
HENRY CHALK.